LABORATORY AT THE
BOTTOM OF THE WORLD

Laboratory at the Bottom of the World

by PETER BRIGGS

DAVID McKAY COMPANY, INC.
New York

LABORATORY AT THE BOTTOM OF THE WORLD

COPYRIGHT © 1970 BY PETER BRIGGS

Library of Congress Catalog Card Number: 76-132161

MANUFACTURED IN THE UNITED STATES OF AMERICA

VAN REES PRESS • NEW YORK

*My particular thanks to the
National Science Foundation and
the United States Navy.*

CONTENTS

blackouts. Whistlers and lightning. Airglow. Low-frequency radio waves. Plans for automating Byrd Station. Listening in on Apollo 11. Solar flares and space flight. The shape of the world by satellite.

Photographs follow page 118

LABORATORY AT THE
BOTTOM OF THE WORLD

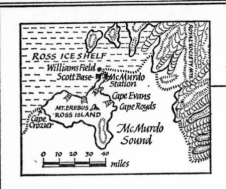

ANTARCTICA

0 200 400 600 800 1000 2000 miles

★ U.S. Stations ■ Other Stations ● Combined Stations

ROSS ICE SHELF
— Williams Field ●
Scott Base ■ ● McMurdo Station
Cape Evans
Cape Royds
MT. EREBUS
ROSS ISLAND
Cape Crozier
McMurdo Sound

0 10 20 30 40 miles

ROYAL SOCIETY MTS.

SOUTH AFRICA

Indian Ocean

South Atlantic Ocean

South Pacific Ocean

Weddell Sea

BRITISH, CHILEAN, ARGENTINE BASES
Palmer Station
SOUTH AMERICA
Bellingshausen Sea

USSR
JAPAN
USSR
AUSTRALIA
AUSTRALIA
UNITED KINGDOM
ARGENTINA
FILCHNER ICE SHELF
Plateau Station
TRANS-ANTARCTIC MTS.
South Pole Station
Komsomolskaya
Mirny (USSR)
Vostok
GEOMAGNETIC POLE
Byrd Station
Beardmore Glacier
Site of Fossil Find
MARIE BYRD LAND
ROSS ICE SHELF
AUSTRALIA
McMurdo Station
Scott Base
Ross Sea
Adélie Coast
FRANCE
Hallett Station
ANTARCTIC CIRCLE

30
0
30
60
60
90
90
120
120
150
150 E.
180
65
75
85

South Pacific Ocean

TASMANIA
NEW ZEALAND
AUSTRALIA

Ascherl

CHAPTER I

THE GREAT EXPERIMENT BEGINS

A GOOD and happy revolution makes few headlines in times as sensational as ours. The gift of a whole
continent to the pursuit of knowledge, even if it is the
coldest and most desolate place on earth, does not have the
same visceral effect as, well, choose your own favorite
disaster from this morning's news. What has very quietly
happened is that the entire Antarctic has become the ex-
clusive province of the scientists, and what they are doing
is one of the most wholesome, intellectually exciting of all
contemporary stories. The adventures going on in the
minds of some of the most brilliant men of our time and
the international spirit of good will being displayed at the
bottom of the world offer some hope for those who stub-
bornly believe that man really does have a future.

This great experiment began with a treaty that went
into effect on June 23, 1961. The treaty recognized that
"it is in the interest of all mankind that Antarctica *shall
continue forever* to be used exclusively for peaceful purposes and shall not become the scene or object of international discord." The signers of this treaty were Argentina, Australia, Belgium, Chile, France, Japan, New

Zealand, Norway, South Africa, Russia, Great Britain, and the United States. Four other nations signed the document later.

The fifth largest continent in the world, made famous by the exploits of individual heroes and defamed by the hunters who practically exterminated the whales and the fur seals, suddenly became a place of great honor and expectations.

The treaty is a remarkable act, something that has never happened before in human history. That it occurred at all is due primarily to those supposedly impotent politicians, the scientists. Beginning in the early 1950s, groups of these men, many of them Americans and most of them geophysicists, started a campaign for a world-wide program of research into such questions as the nature of the world's magnetism, the geography of the upper atmosphere, the effects of solar flares, the shape of the world and the dynamics of its masses of sea and land. Many of these geophysical questions could be answered only by simultaneous measurements of phenomena at various places on the earth at precisely the same time. The idea of the program was developed at numerous meetings of international scientific societies. It was received with enthusiasm by many researchers, including those from the Soviet Union. As it finally developed, the only large nation that abstained was Communist China. The major criticism of the original proposals was that too much of the work was centered on the Antarctic, and so the program was broadened to answer these objections. The final name for the project was the International Geophysical Year, the IGY, and the date was set for 1957 and 1958, when the sun would be at a time of maximum activity.

Then the scientists went to their governments with what

was almost an accomplished fact to ask for material support. Ever since World War II, governments in developed countries had been actively supporting scientific research and, even if many politicians did not truly understand what geophysics was all about, the scientists, not all of them amateurs at public relations, had made the program of the IGY seem so grand, so advanced, so worthwhile that the governments of sixty-six nations finally supported the effort in varying degrees. The most famous events of the IGY were the Russian launching of the world's first artificial satellite, Sputnik, and the American discovery of the Van Allen radiation belt.

A large proportion of the U.S. Government backing for the IGY went into Antarctic projects, as the nation had been sporadically interested in the region for more than a century. Ever since the time of the Greek philosophers, men had thought there should be a continent at the bottom of the world, if only to balance things off, but the first serious attempt to find it was that of Captain Cook of the British Navy late in the eighteenth century. Cook was not able to sight any land because the ice pack held him at bay. He did cross the Antarctic Circle, however, made water from salt-free ice, saw birds he felt must have nested on land, and concluded that some land had to exist farther south than he could penetrate, but that it was certainly uninhabited. The first American discoverer in the Southern Ocean was Captain Nat Palmer of Connecticut who, at the age of twenty, was in charge of a seal-hunting ship that weighed only forty tons. In this small craft he ventured south of Deception Island, a favorite harbor for sealers, and found the land mass called the Palmer Peninsula. On his return north he was surprised to be overhauled by a much larger Russian vessel cap-

tained by the Baron von Bellingshausen. The Russian explorer was surprised that such a young man in such a
small vessel had found the continent before him, but
he generously conceded the American's precedence and
named the new territory Palmer's Land on his maps.

The next Americans in Antarctic history were Charles
Eights, who traveled far south on an expedition partly
financed by Palmer, writing seven scientific papers about
his trip, and Lieutenant Charles Wilkes of the U.S. Navy
who with a fleet of five ships in 1840 sailed as far south as
he could, traveled 1500 miles along the edge of the ice,
and sighted enough mountain peaks to be sure he had observed a continent. At about the same time the French sent
out an exploring expedition led by Dumont d'Urville and
the English launched one led by James Clark Ross. It was
Ross who discovered the sea and the ice shelf now named
after him and also McMurdo Sound, named after his first
lieutenant, the site of the present U.S. station. Ross also
found two great mountains, Erebus and Terror, which he
named after his ships.

Whaling and sealing continued in the Antarctic, but
interest in exploration there lapsed for many years after
the activity of the 1840s. Then, around the beginning of
the twentieth century, for reasons not very clear today, a
number of men in Europe and the United States caught
polar fever. Americans and some Norwegians were willing
to face death in order to be the first man at the North Pole.
An American, Robert Peary, reached it in 1909. Some
Englishmen found the South Pole more of a challenge,
but a Norwegian, Roald Amundsen, led the first exploring
party to stand on it. In this romantic "age of heroes,"
Amundsen and the Englishmen, Robert Scott and Ernest
Shackleton, proved that man might get to the South Pole

(or at least near it), but at a terrible cost and with few scientific dividends, simply proving that it could be done if men were willing to pay the price.

The United States returned to the Antarctic in 1929 when a Navy officer, Richard E. Byrd, set up a privately financed base at Little America on the Ross Ice Shelf. Byrd began to show that the Antarctic would only really be explored when large amounts of men, equipment, and the airplane, the vehicle that can simply jump over the terrifying crevasses and impassable mountains, were brought into action. At the same time it became clear that an airplane is a vehicle that requires many men on the ground to support the airborne daredevils.

Byrd's 1933–34 expedition to Little America, during which the airplane came even more into use, was still a very primitive affair. Speaking recently, Kennett L. Rawson, a book publisher today but who was in Byrd's party as a young man, remarked, "Logistics was ninety-nine percent of the game. Science got the other one percent. And a day that wasn't miserable was a good day." Survival took so much time that little research could be done.

The U.S. Government, which had given some assistance to all Byrd's former expeditions, formally declared itself in the business of Antarctic exploration with Operation High Jump from October to March in 1946–47, the months when the sun never sets. Admiral Byrd had 4000 men and 13 ships under his command. This remains today the most massive assault by one nation on the continent. High Jump's major achievements were a hundred exploratory flight missions (often undertaken from aircraft carriers), the discovery of about 350,000 square miles of previously unknown territory, and photographs of about sixty percent of the continent's coastline, a quarter of which had never been seen before. Hundreds of new mountain peaks were found as well as twenty-six new islands. High Jump showed what technology could do but also demonstrated its limitations. All those marvelous photographs were useless for map-making until the less ambitious Operation Windmill the following year sent helicopters ashore from icebreakers to land on and survey fixed points, obvious from the pictures, so that the mass of filmed data could be oriented. To understand the Antarctic fully, it came to be realized, man had to occupy it physically.

(It should perhaps be noted here that numerous other governments besides that of the United States, and one private U.S. expedition led by Commander Finn Ronne, were also exploring the Antarctic during these years.)

When the United States decided officially to support the International Geophysical Year, the difficult job of supporting the scientists was given to the Navy, the service with the best experience and equipment for the work. A small task force of ships sailed for the Antarctic in the southern summer of 1955 to set up a base from which the planned inland station, to be named after Admiral Byrd, would be supplied. The task force also sought a base where large planes could land on the ice and which could be used to support parties going to the South Pole and other locations. The base that would be used to establish Byrd Station was found at the edge of the Ross Ice Shelf and named Little America V. Then the small group of ships sailed to McMurdo Sound where, it was decided after a process of elimination, the air station would have to be built. The Americans had little experience around McMurdo but the area had been used frequently by Scott and Shackleton for their assaults on the

Pole. The ice was thick enough to support landings by heavy aircraft but, only a few miles away, the ice usually cleared out completely for a month or more every year and ships could come right up to the shore to discharge. More than that, between the proposed airstrip on ice and the seaport there was solid land, or at least volcanic rubble, on which buildings could be erected that would not tumble into the sea whenever an ice shelf calved a new iceberg. Best of all, McMurdo was the nearest good base for flights from New Zealand and, at the same time, as close to the South Pole as any possible seaport.

On December 17, 1955, the Navy Seabees arrived at McMurdo to erect housing and clear an ice runway. Within two days they had prepared an 8000-foot airstrip on the thick ice, and on December 20, good weather being promised, eight U.S. planes took off from Christchurch, New Zealand, to fly non-stop 2230 miles to the new McMurdo Station. Four aircraft had to turn back because headwinds used up a dangerous amount of their fuel supply, but four other planes, two Neptunes and two Sky-masters, made it with studied nonchalance. This historic journey marked the first time that aircraft had reached the Antarctic from an outside base. With the runway success-fully completed, the Seabees began to improve the tem-porary land accommodations at the base that was sup-posed to last only a few years.

The following year, on October 31, 1956, Rear Admiral George Dufek, in charge of what was known as Operation Deep Freeze, took off from McMurdo and landed at the South Pole. When he stepped out of his plane, he was the first human being to stand there since Scott's ill-fated ex-pedition in January 1912. Only seventeen human beings had ever been there before. When the Admiral landed, the

temperature was 58 degrees below zero and the wind blew
at ten knots. With difficulty the Admiral and his crew
chipped a hole in the ice to plant a U.S. flag. Some pictures
were taken; other cameras froze. Finally, after a little
more than a half-hour, their faces obviously getting frostbitten, one of the men said to his commander, "Boss, I
can't move the fingers of this hand. I think they're frozen.
We've done everything here we can. I suggest we leave."

"Good," the Admiral replied. "Let's get the hell out of
here." The aircraft engines had been kept running and the
plane had jet bottles to assist on the take-off, but it took
every bit of power they had before the plane could clear
the ice.

Because of the cold at the Pole, the Admiral deferred
beginning a base there until November 19, when a Globemaster flew to the Pole to take its temperature. "Men can
work at the temperatures (50 below) at sea level but not
at 10,000 feet." One week later a scouting Globemaster
reported a mild 29 degrees below, so after midnight, with
a bright sun, two ski-equipped planes landed at the South
Pole with one Navy lieutenant, seven trained men, and
eleven huskies. The Admiral observed all this action from
a Globemaster and then his plane parachuted a tractor,
sleds, and other equipment to the men below. Seabees
arrived a few days later to help construct the base, and on
November 26 ten more men were flown in. When weather
allowed, three airlifts a day each parachuted ten tons of
supplies. The South Pole Station was born. Planned for
only three years, it has been continuously occupied ever
since.

Before the IGY officially began, U.S. forces had constructed three more Antarctic bases. One, named for
Lincoln Ellsworth, the American who in 1935 was the first

to fly across Antarctica, was established on the edge of the Weddell Sea, an ocean covered with ice that is singularly unknown and bleak. Another was called Hallett, after the cape of that name in Victoria Land, one of the first points on the continent reached on the flight from New Zealand. The third, named Wilkes after the early American explorer, was on the Antarctic coast at one of the points closest to Australia. All this construction in a hostile environment was, naturally, done at some cost. A number of deaths and injuries happened due to airplane accidents. Several men lost their lives falling into crevasses. The dollar value of the U.S. effort has not been possible to compute, since military costs would have continued in any case, but it is estimated that it took about a million dollars to establish and support each man stationed at the South Pole.

The Russian IGY program in the Antarctic began with the establishment on the coast of a base which they called Mirny (Peaceful), after the name of one of Baron von Bellingshausen's ships which explored these southern waters in 1820. Mirny is south of Australia and South Africa at a point in between about equidistant from both lands. Moving inland by tractor (the Russians considered their ultimate goals to be at too great an altitude for aircraft), they first established a small station, Pionerskaya, 230 miles inland. The men who wintered over here were the first ever to do so on this largest Antarctic plateau. Plans for the 1957 summer were to reach the permanent station to be called Vostok, near the geomagnetic pole. The start was delayed when the icebreaker *Lena*, moored to an ice cliff that towered high above it, was nearly sunk after a great slab of ice broke loose and fell on the ship's deck. Two men were killed and the expedition could not start out until a quite elaborate funeral was mounted for the victims. Then one of the barracks burned to the ground and the party could not set out until it was rebuilt. At the end of February, very late in the summer season, they finally set forth, only to be bogged down soon by snows that had not been packed by high winds and by the 12,000-foot elevation that kept their Diesel tractor engines working at only sixty percent of sea-level efficiency. In March they realized they could not possibly reach their destination before darkness set in, and reluctantly, to avoid almost certain death, they dug in for the winter at a camp provisionally named Vostok I. The following summer vast amounts of supplies were shipped into Mirny. Much of this was shipped overland to Vostok I but additional fuel was flown to a new station called Komsomolskaya. This was a sort of crossroads for the turn east to the proposed Vostok Station and the turn west to the very distant Pole of Inaccessibility, the point of land in the Antarctic farthest distant from any seacoast. Vostok was reached on December 16, 1957, and then the much more difficult assault on the Pole of Inaccessibility began. The party on this mission, troubled by the soft snow and the altitude, had to stop for the winter on February 10, 1958, at a base they named Sovietskaya, 400 miles from their destination. The five men left to winter there spent a terrible season, due to the cold and the altitude. The men at Vostok were not much better off. They recorded a record temperature of 125.3 degrees below zero. It is likely that Sovietskaya had equally cold weather, but their thermometers were not calibrated for such extremes. To reach the Pole of Inaccessibility the following spring, before the end of the IGY, a dash began directly from Mirny. A fast-moving force of eighteen men on four tractors, supported by airborne fuel on the first part of their trip, traveled the 1360 miles in fifty-two days. The scientists found time to stop at intervals to make gravity and seismic soundings. At the Pole of Inaccessibility drills in the deep ice showed that the average temperature was 73 degrees below zero. The ice was 9500 feet deep, and their camp was 12,000 feet above sea level.

When Australians learned that Russia would build IGY bases on Antarctic territory that Australia had claimed, the local newspapers predictably complained. Australian distress was compounded by the fact that Soviet power would be established so close to their country, although Mirny, the nearest base, was almost 3000 miles away. The clamor died down eventually, and Australia set up a major station named after their most prominent Antarctic explorer, Douglas Mawson. They also established Davis Station, about 400 miles east of Mirny, and shared the facilities of Wilkes Station with the United States (which later transferred the entire base to them). Australians were particularly interested in studies of the ice, but were also active in cosmic ray research and geology.

Japan's IGY program in the Antarctic was beset by misfortune. The site allocated, west of Australia's Mawson Station, was very difficult to reach from the sea. The Japanese sent not an icebreaker but a lighthouse tender named the *Soya* which repeatedly became stuck in the ice. The U.S. icebreaker *Glacier* tried to help the ship but was unsuccessful. The following year the *Soya* did reach the coast and the Japanese flag was flown over Showa Station. (Showa is the name the present Emperor will receive on his death.) When the *Soya* tried to sail in February 1957, it again could not penetrate the ice and the Russian ship *Ob* had to rescue it. The following year the *Soya* returned

once more and this time the U.S.S. *Burton Island* tried to
help it. Neither vessel could get close enough to land
supplies for the next winter and finally the eleven men at
the station, along with one husky and her eight pups,
were lifted out by air. Fifteen huskies had to be left behind to care for themselves. The abandonment of the
station, half-way through the IGY, and the treatment of
the dogs caused quite a stir in Japan. A monument was
erected at Osaka in honor of the animals. The *Soya* returned again the following year, however, and found that
two of the dogs were still alive. Evidently they had survived on penguins and the dried milk that had been left
behind for them. Once more the *Soya* became trapped in
the ice but this time managed to free itself after twenty-
six days. The Japanese scientific research mostly concerned
the ionosphere and cosmic rays.

Belgium, Norway, Argentina, Chile, Great Britain, New
Zealand, and France also established scientific bases at
various positions around the Antarctic continent. Geophysical subjects were the main concern in all these
nations' research. Few of them were spared some kind of
troubles, either with vehicles tumbling into crevasses, airplanes having accidents, or with a number of disastrous
fires. These particularly plagued the Chilean and Argentinian stations on Palmer Peninsula (which the English
call Graham Land. By compromise, the whole area is now
called the Antarctic Peninsula.). This peninsula had eleven
British stations, seven Argentinian, and four Chilean, because all three nations claim this land which lies directly
below South America, to which it is related geologically
and geographically. None of the three disputants wanted
the others to be able to claim that they had neglected it.
The wonder is that there was no serious friction during the

IGY in the Antarctic except that on the Palmer Peninsula, which never went too far. Greater wonder may be that the Russians and the Americans got along so well. Of course, they were usually separated by many hundreds of miles, but scientists were exchanged who dwelt in harmony at one another's bases, and this contact seems to have done a good deal for relations, at least in this part of the world.

When the IGY officially ended in 1958, the idea of international scientific cooperation seemed to have scored a considerable victory, particularly in the Antarctic.

The IGY brought great technological advances to the Antarctic. Permanent bases established deep within the continent by both the United States and Russia were probably the most spectacular achievements of men and machines. Aviation made great strides, and not much area remained that had never been seen, at least from the air. Sixteen parties from eight countries made land traverses that covered 14,000 miles of ice. The most publicized of these was the Commonwealth Trans-Antarctic Expedition led by Vivian Fuchs that traveled by vehicle from the Weddell Sea to the South Pole and then on to Scott Base at McMurdo Sound. Fuchs' party was aided by air drops of fuel and provisions and by the caches of material deposited between McMurdo and the South Pole by Sir Edmund Hillary, the first man ever to climb Mount Everest. On his passage Fuchs made numerous soundings to determine the depth of the ice beneath him, to help answer the question of whether the continent was one mass of land or several.

Other traverses in the same general area also aimed to find out what lies underneath the ice. Some soundings at Byrd Station (see map) showed that it rested on 8300 feet of ice although the elevation above sea level was just a bit more than 5000 feet. Presumably if all the ice at Byrd Station melted the area would be under water. Earlier soundings suggested that the Antarctic might be divided in two, that, if the great plateau of ice did not exist, the area between Weddell and Ross seas would be covered by water. One traverse of Marie Byrd Land, through which such a connecting sea would have to pass, seemed to show that the rock below the ice was indeed below sea level. Other traverses contradicted this finding. One such survey seemed to show that the Ross and Weddell seas did not connect but that the Bellingshausen Sea, on the other side of the Palmer Peninsula from the Weddell, did connect with the Ross. The soundings from all these traverses are still spread too widely apart to provide a complete map of what lies underneath.

During these traverses several mountain ranges were explored that previously had only been seen at a distance from the air. The Sentinel Mountains, which had seemed to exist by themselves, turned out to be an extension of the range of the Palmer Peninsula, itself an extension of the Andes. The low Horlick Mountains, due south of Byrd Station and only 300 miles from the Pole, contained very extensive beds of coal. (The Antarctic may turn out to be one of the greatest coal fields on earth.)

Much research went into the many questions concerning the Antarctic ice. The first attempts to penetrate it using oil drilling gear began at Byrd Station. Holes were also dug on the Ross Ice Shelf, an area the size of France. Which glaciers did the most to replenish it? Did the Ross ice grow in part from freezing at the bottom? The great question was whether the whole volume of Antarctic ice was increasing or waning. Surveys showed that twice as much of the world's water was bound up in it as had been previously estimated. (This is a matter of some current consequence.) Finally, concerning ice, the Russians declared that they had found the world's largest glacier and they named it the IGY. (The Australians had called it the Lambert Glacier.) Russian calculations showed that this river of ice was about 800 miles long and 370 miles wide. On the question of whether the Antarctic was one body of land or more, earthquake studies seemed to show that the East Antarctic at least, the side facing Australia and South Africa, was certainly one great mass. Studies of birds had not been planned, but at the Russian Mirny and the U.S. Wilkes stations, penguin rookeries were so near that scientists could not resist making population counts. Researchers at Wilkes captured some little Adélie penguins, flew them several thousand miles to McMurdo Station, then released them to test their powers of navigation. Many months later some of the banded Adélies had managed to find their way to their natural home near Wilkes.

At the end of the IGY, it was the Russians who suggested that the international cooperation be continued. Research in the Antarctic, particularly, had only just begun and there was as yet only a small return on what had been a great investment. The international weather network alone, in the Antarctic, made a continuation of the project worthwhile.

On December 25, 1958, the Soviet Union's chief scientist in the Antarctic, Dr. Eugene Tolstikov, flew with a party of eight in an Ilyushin IL-12, an airplane similar to the American DC-3, from the station at Mirny over the South Pole, which they used as a radio checkpoint, and then landed at McMurdo Sound. There they were greeted by U.S. Rear Admiral Dufek. Dr. Tolstikov told a press conference at McMurdo that it was essential that the momentum achieved in Antarctic research and exploration be continued. "The nations studying the Antarctic continent should pursue the scientific objectives together, but each should continue to work in the regions where their respective IGY programs have been pressed." Then the Russian party proceeded on their flight, which was to survey routes for a proposed tractor trek to the Bellingshausen Sea the following year.

An Australian, Philip Law, leader of that country's activities in the southern continent, saw another benefit to research down there. The dangerous environment had resulted in a great change of feeling about political differences: "The era of territorial competition of the first 50 years of this century has given way to an era of technological competition, in which nations use the arena accorded by the Antarctic to demonstrate their technical and scientific skills.... I believe that the international amity and good will which have characterized the IGY in Antarctica will extend beyond scientific circles and contribute towards improved international relations in general and a broader understanding between peoples."

Scientists from most countries had presented to their governments the idea that the IGY would be a one-shot affair, and there was some reluctance to go back to the heads of state and ask for more assistance. The Russians, however, had said they wanted to continue in the Antarctic, which meant that the United States would certainly not pull out, and so questions of national prestige everywhere became involved. There was no general international declaration that Antarctic research would continue, but no country announced that it was ceasing activity there.

At this stage the United States brought up the treaty for the Antarctic that it had proposed first in 1948, only to have it fall on deaf ears. This time the climate was right. Cooperation had been successful, there was no compelling argument against the idea, and it was clear that scientific dividends were sure to be forthcoming. No powerful nation could afford to ignore completely the desires of its scientists, because national economies had become more and more dependent on the results scientists might produce. The scientists, of course, were very happy to be given a whole continent as a laboratory for their studies.

Diplomacy is a slow business, and the Antarctic treaty did not go into official force until 1961. Meanwhile researchers kept up much of the momentum from the colossal IGY effort. Their work has continued, and the precedent for peaceful cooperation between nations which has been established in that part of the world may, in time, be recognized as the sort of cooperation that should be going on everywhere in the world, not just in science but in helping the poorer countries lift themselves out of the quicksand of poverty, illiteracy, and overpopulation, and in controlling technology everywhere before it pollutes the human race out of existence.

Meanwhile, before the millennium arrives, several thousand men each year go down to the Antarctic, at a considerable cost to their governments, to face the hard work, the dangers, and the isolated conditions of its rigorous environment. They are not all dedicated scientists, of course, and living conditions are not usually so extreme that they can all consider themselves heroes. But even the

men in the military, who are there only because they have
been given orders to go, are involuntarily contributing to
knowledge. To a man cursing a frozen bolt, a broken axle,
a dead radio, a burned-out engine, a man keeping his
sanity during the monotony of long months of winter
darkness, a mention of the glorious role of science would
probably produce just another strong epithet. But the
science is there, and it is beginning to pay off. Logistics
is no longer ninety-nine percent of the scientists' game.
(For the U.S. researchers, the Navy's Operation Deep
Freeze takes care of almost all of that.) The scientist is
freed to pursue his true goals. A geologist may complain
that he has to wait two days for a helicopter to give him
a one-hour lift to the site he wants to explore. When he is
delivered, with tent, provisions, and a convenient little
motor toboggan in which he can travel at speeds up to
twenty miles an hour or more, he may seem unaware that
without this outside support he would have had to slog
for weeks over mountains, ice, terrible crevasses, with
desperate temperatures and fierce winds, to reach his desired goal. Physically, it has become a good deal easier
over the years to pursue the elusive secrets waiting for
discovery at the end of the world.

But all this activity has been going on for quite a long
time now, and the United States alone has already in-
vested about a quarter of a billion dollars in its share of
the program. Has it been worth it or will it be in the
future?

The author was fortunate enough recently to be given
a fairly good look at the present situation as the guest of
the government's National Science Foundation and the
U.S. Navy. He talked with many of the scientists at work
on scores of projects and with the personnel, civilian and

Navy, who are backing them up. He became fascinated with the atmosphere men have created in the Antarctic without planning to do so, and he was awed speechless by the natural wonders of the place. He considered the trip the most remarkable one it is possible to take in this world, but that is not the point of writing about it.

The purpose is to report on what one observer learned about the scientists' continent. Has this vast research program been worthwhile?

CHAPTER II

WILL WE ALL FREEZE TOGETHER OR DROWN?

THE instant response to mention of Antarctica seems to be the word "cold," almost immediately followed by the word "ice." The North Pole and Greenland are famous for having ice, too, but nothing in the world compares to the ice sheet of the Antarctic. For a rough idea of its extent, consider the rather familiar contours of the United States, Mexico, and the Gulf of Mexico, and try to visualize all this area under ice that is in some places three miles thick. The Antarctic is somewhat larger than this, and ninety-eight percent of it is invisible under its white cover. In addition, in winter the thick ice extends hundreds of miles out to sea. One afternoon early in November, I was in an airplane flying at 30,000 feet across the vast Southern Ocean, looking down to get my first glimpse of this extraordinary phenomenon.

The fact of my being somewhere near the Antarctic Circle was one of those things you know are true although you still do not feel it. It is the same feeling one has trying to digest absolutely extraordinary and unexpected news. You believe it at the top of your head but it still does not seem quite true. I had known about this trip for several months, but it had all worked out so casually that it was not very real. While working on a book about the unsolved mysteries of science I had gotten in touch with a young man named Peter Barrett to find out more details of the discovery that had sent most conservative U.S. geophysicists into a tailspin. Poking about rocks in the Trans-Antarctic Mountains, Mr. Barrett had found the fossil bone of a vertebrate animal, an animal known to have lived in the distant past in South America and South Africa. No vertebrate land animal fossil had ever been discovered in the Antarctic before. To find the remains of one at last with close relatives on other continents suggested very strongly that things were not today as they had always been in the past. That ancient animal, a fresh-water amphibian known as a labyrinthodont, was not very likely to have swum across several thousand miles of salt water in order to die high up on a mountain. The best way to explain the presence of that bone was to call on the theory of continental drift, the idea that land masses now far apart were once joined. How else could the labyrinthodont have reached his present grave?

While talking with Barrett about finding a bone in the Antarctic, I found my mind straying away from scientific mysteries in general and onto the subject of the fossil find. I had found out much more than I needed for the book then in progress, but Barrett's discovery by itself, although extremely important to science, did not at the time seem to have enough narrative in it to warrant full-length treatment. I talked with my publisher about it and that expansive gentleman saw no problem at all. "Why not write about all Antarctic science today?" This idea sounded very grand and tempting (I did not quite realize

then how much was going on), so the same day I asked
the National Science Foundation, the government office
that finances most basic research, if they had room for one
more body on their next press trip to the bottom of the
world. I was so late in asking that I hardly dared hope
I could make it, but, a few days later, a phone call told
me that a man had dropped out of the party and I could
come along. The writer's trip to one of the great wonders
of the world began in this rather casual manner.

First, in September, most of the people going down
under the auspices of the National Science Foundation,
familiarly referred to as the NSF, met at the Skylands
Lodge in the Shenandoah National Park in Virginia. There
we had a few days of orientation lectures, talks and films
about the Antarctic, a taste of what was to come. I shared
a cabin with a young Navy lieutenant who was on his
way to Palmer Station where he would be in charge during
the long winter night. How did his newly married wife
feel about this long period of absence? She felt that, if
he had to be overseas, such an isolated base would keep
him safely out of mischief. For himself, like most men
planning to winter over, the lieutenant planned to do a
great deal of serious reading. During the orientation course
I met Admiral Dufek, the man who had been in charge
of the Navy's preparation for IGY, and a number of prominent scientists I ran into later in much different circumstances. The orientation was valuable, but it seemed
very slim fare when one was finally confronted with the
reality of the Antarctic itself. The actual flight from Washington, D.C., began about four o'clock one morning in
November.

With space satellites rocketing around the world in just
ninety minutes, a flight that takes you to New Zealand in

either two days or three, depending on whether you count crossing the International Date Line, does not seem very unusual to read about. Commercial planes do this regularly. Military air transport is different, however. The planes are basically enormous cargo ships. Passenger seats, though comfortable enough, are just temporary furniture that can be dismantled in a few minutes. Cargo has no need for windows and so, when passengers are aboard, there are only four windows for all of them to share. Though traveling half-way around the world, all one could get a look at were the airports of San Francisco, Honolulu, Pago Pago, and Christchurch, N.Z.

The true spectacular began after a day and a half of military courtesy and efficiency in the little New Zealand city just beginning to bloom with a profusion of spring flowers. (Remember, the seasons are reversed below the Equator.) Rear Admiral Welch, the officer in charge of all the U.S. Naval support forces in the Antarctic program, gave the visitors a reception soon after landing. The next day visitors received a staggering amount of entirely novel and entirely necessary cold-weather clothing. The special thermal boots, which weigh about ten pounds, must fit perfectly. Once equipped, the visitors, who included representatives of the nations that signed the treaty designed to keep the Antarctic forever peaceful, scientists, most of them very young, who would stay "on the ice" either for the brief summer season or for the year-long wintering over, and the eight guest journalists, were all free to see the sights of Christchurch. It was soon discovered that the rigid local laws about Sundays (even movies were not open) did not apply to drinks at the Officer's Club.

Before nine the next morning all the passengers were

buckled in their seats, seats made of nothing but red cloth webbing, much like erect deck chairs. Surprisingly, they were very comfortable. Accommodations for passengers could be quickly removed to make room for large pieces of cargo. The plane could easily carry two full-sized city buses and could actually transport an entire small nuclear power plant, compartmentalized into units each the dimensions of a good-sized room. This prop-driven plane, the Hercules, which could convert from wheels to skis in mid-air, was not originally designed for Antarctic work at all, but the military discovered that it was the best aircraft ever developed for long-distance polar work. (Helicopters are invaluable, too.)

The Hercules, affectionately known as the Herc, is fast for a non-jet; it cruises at more than 300 miles an hour at altitudes around 30,000 feet. The passengers were invited to the flight deck (which civilians might call the pilot's cabin), and most people took a brief look, but there was nothing to see but the South Pacific Ocean far, far below. That whitecaps were visible suggested that the sea down there was not as calm and comfortable as we were at our sunlit altitude. We were actually over the sailors' dreaded "Roaring Forties." Crewmen distributed coffee and sweet rolls and the passengers began to walk around and socialize.

Taking advantage of our flight deck privilege I kept going forward frequently as the day progressed to get a first look at the famous ice sheet. At last, over the roar of our engines, the co-pilot told me those white things I was seeing down there were icebergs. Then the mountains of ice seemed spaced closer and closer together until suddenly the great ice cap appeared. We were still quite a distance from the coast but, at our speed, the first mountains of

Victoria Land loomed reassuringly on the radar (our pilots had found the continent, after all this water) and soon we were over them. A seemingly endless line of black peaks thrust themselves above the engulfing whiteness. In spite of the noise of the airplane, it all seemed absolutely silent and motionless down there outside the pilots' window. The vast landscape, so solid and timeless, so absolutely unchanged by our intrusion, made the Hercules appear to be nothing more than a rude insect. The plane's course kept us over the range for half an hour or so, and the cabin began to fill up with sightseers like myself. Though I greedily wanted to look at more, I relinquished my vantage point and climbed down the little ladder back to my seat. From this position I could see just enough through a distant window to realize that we had passed over the mountains and onto the Ross Ice Shelf itself.

Our National Science Foundation guardian, Jack Renirie, awoke from a comfortable nap about this time and I, in great excitement, pointed to the window so he wouldn't miss the sight. Jack, who lives near Washington, D.C., has been coming down to the "ice" for seven years and, in fact, had made the trip up from McMurdo only three days before, smiled politely, though he seemed to understand my enthusiasm, and then he began to put on his survival gear.

Soon everyone, about seventy men and the lady aboard, Jean Pearson, the delightful science editor of the *Detroit News,* began this rather clumsy operation. Those of us new to this already unusual trip had boarded the plane in balmy Christchurch wearing our own underwear, over which we had on long drawers and undershirts called thermal underwear, then green shirts and pants of a rather heavy cotton mixture. I wore tennis shoes and the others wore something similar. Now we added to this heavier green trousers with a woolen liner. These pants had many pockets. The green coat that reached almost to the knees was also lined with wool and had countless pockets. For our heads there was a pile-lined cap with flaps that would pull down over the ears and a parka that could be buttoned to the coat with a furry edge that could be drawn over the cap. For our hands there were woolen gloves, to be covered with black leather gloves, and over all this great fur-backed mittens popularly called bear-paws. The fur backs were to wipe your nose, which tends to run in extreme cold. For our feet there were thermal boots, of many layers, the outside of which seemed to be made of rubber. These laced half-way up the calves and were called bunny boots. Add to this sunglasses, camera equipment, a small bag with a toothbrush and similar things, and you have quite a bulky package. All this must be taken with you whenever you leave one of the U.S. bases, even for a brief helicopter ride. Later I learned the why of the matter in a way, though not immediately personal, that convinced me that this was not just another outmoded military regulation.

(I had already noticed aboard our Navy Hercules, in spite of the presence of the commanding admiral and also a second admiral, an engineer on an inspection tour of the installations, a distinct absence of that petty insistence on rank and privilege that annoys the American civilian who suddenly finds himself an enlisted man. The admirals were treated with considerable respect, a certain number of "Yes, sir's" and "No, sir's" were overheard, but the atmosphere was by no means military. I also saw a certain amount of saluting at McMurdo and wondered how anyone could distinguish between ranks when everyone wore much the same clothes. The enlisted men did eat in a separate cafeteria but were served exactly the same food. They also had separate clubs, where only beer was allowed, but I suspect that some indulgent officers also made whiskey available to enlisted men in cases of the polar equivalent snake-bite or other emergency.)

Fully dressed now according to the rules, the newcomers peered eagerly out the windows as the Herc began its descent. "There's Erebus" a friendly crewman pointed to the famous smoking volcano in an offhand manner, and there it certainly was, covered to the top of its cone in ice that seemed blue-green and smoking as advertised. We lost the volcano as we came down behind some lower hills, then the Base was pointed out, and suddenly we were down on the snow in what seemed a bumpy landing. I learned later that it was a very excellent landing and that coming down on ice, with skis, is like coming down on a choppy sea with pontoons.

We left the plane by rank, the admirals first, then the representatives of foreign nations; the press found themselves third in rank. They were followed by the scientists, and then, finally, by the enlisted passengers. Hands all encumbered, the jump from the last rung on the ladder to the snow was a little bit longer than one is used to.

Crunching about on the snow, waiting to be photographed as "distinguished visitors," it seemed wintry but not really cold. Sunglasses were definitely required, and I understood immediately what snow-blindness meant. Uppermost was the thought, "I really *am* in the Antarctic!" and the hands, new at this game, walked around smiling at each other as if they had actually done something spectacular. There might be something a little childish about this general reaction, but I think not. The Antarctic is still a rather difficult and unusual place to get to.

Several small buses waited for the passengers to drive them from Williams Field (where the buildings and storage tanks for fuel have been set down in such a way that they can be quickly hauled to safety by tractor if the ice underneath should start to break up). McMurdo Base itself is six miles away over the frozen Sound. The course on the glaring white surface is marked by red flags at frequent intervals, there are drums of gasoline along the way for safety's sake, the bus driver must report to Operations by voice radio when he leaves Williams itself and report again when he has arrived at the main base.

These precautions seemed extreme during the sunny afternoon when we arrived. However, a condition known as a "whiteout" may occur very suddenly, a situation where the sky and snow-covered ice seem to blend, when there is no horizon, and men become hopelessly disoriented and lost. Being marooned out on this highway, perhaps for many hours while the temperature is well below freezing, could very well be a fatal experience if no one knew you were there and no one sent a party to rescue you. For similar reasons, no one is permitted to walk outside McMurdo Base without a companion and the Operations Office must be informed of your departure and return.

Then our little bus ground up a rather steep, rough, but short hill and we were at McMurdo itself. Many of the men walking busily about their business were wearing only woolen lumberjack shirts, and the news was that the temperature stood at the spectacular high of 28 degrees above. The old hands, whether they had arrived only two days before or had spent the whole year, wintering over, made us feel very much like rookies. The bus drove around the small town, depositing Mrs. Pearson, our colleague, at the new National Science Foundation quarters for distinguished scientists (the main problem about women in the Antarctic was that nothing had been built to offer them any privacy), then on to the Ross Hilton, a Quonset hut where the diplomats disembarked, and then a short block away to the Press Hut, our home away from home. It was no more of a Hilton than the diplomats' quarters. There were two double bunks in each small cubicle, the plumbing was a block away, but it was very clean, warm, there was a big press room in which to work, a case of beer cooling on the floor, and the Navy and NSF public relations people who kept us informed and out of trouble during the whole trip. Chow (dinner) began at 5:30 and was served until 7:00. If you missed this, another meal was available at 11:30 P.M., basically for the men going on and off watch. That evening would be ours, free. "Then, men, will you all be ready for the bus at eight o'clock tomorrow morning? Be sure to bring your complete survival gear." In the morning we would get the dramatic flavor of the Antarctic—we would fly to the South Pole, the true end of the world, 800 miles inland, across utterly desolate and uninhabited mountains, across a sheet of ice bigger than the Louisiana Purchase, to that exotic scientific home, the South Pole Station. The following day we would go even farther from McMurdo, to the equally incredible place called Byrd Station, but the Navy would see to it that we always returned to base in time for dinner. In terms of distance these trips were like going from New York to Chicago, meeting some people there and having lunch, and getting back to New York long before sundown. For the passengers, however, the Antarctic trips were much more convenient, as though you were traveling by chartered plane. The difference was that this southern terrain was some of the most exotic territory in the world. It is of considerable importance to the future of the human race that it remain in this condition.

One delegate to a very important scientific congress recently asked, "Are we all going to freeze or will we drown?" His hardly theoretical question concerned the vast ice sheet over which we flew. That endless expanse of white down there, reflecting the sun's glare so strongly that it could not be looked at without dark glasses, seems as though it has been there forever, but it has not. All readers know that a great portion of what is now the United States was covered by ice almost a mile thick as recently as 11,000 years ago. This was long after our very human ancestors had begun to use tools, and later than the time the Indians crossed over from Asia to the Americas. The cave painters of southern France and Spain knew about those glaciers that advanced and retreated not far to the north of them. Written history had not yet begun but the last glacier left records that geologists can read as simply as a book. This ice age was not the first one. In the previous two million years there had been eight others. Is there any reason to suppose that man has seen the last ice age, that another one might not be on the way? Some very respected researchers think we are building up to another period of intense cold and that, considering the rate at which we are modifying our atmosphere and weather, a sheet of ice could build up quite rapidly in Canada to descend upon us. Other men, looking at the Antarctic where something between two or three percent of all the water in the world is locked up in ice, wonder

whether this polar ice cap is melting and if the water released to the oceans from it might not flood all the seacoast cities of the world. If the Antarctic ice turned to
water it would raise sea level everywhere by hundreds
of feet. To ask whether the ice locked up at the Poles is
going through some radical changes, or is resting in a
healthy state of equilibrium, is not being sensational. Most
probably, the behavior of the ice at the North and South
Poles is dependent on the same factors, whatever they
may be. Will our descendants have to run to the hills to
escape the advancing sea or scurry south to beat the
advancing ice? To ask what caused the ice ages and what
the world's vast store of ice is doing today are two ways
of stating the same question. The best answer may be
found in the Antarctic, where most of the ice exists today.

Until the IGY began, something between three and four
million square miles of Antarctic ice had never been seen.
Practically nothing at all was known about the great sheet
inland. What had been studied were bits and pieces
around the continental edge with a few exploratory probes
into the interior. The ice sheet is almost completely within
the Antarctic Circle. Much of it lies below sea level but
no one can accurately say how much at present. If the
ice were removed, the land would recover, raise up, about
one third of the present ice thickness. At the moment, the
Antarctic contains ninety percent of all the ice in the
world, an area of about five million square miles. A thin
layer of snow covers it, snow that becomes ice slowly as
it is pressed down by new layers on top. It does not become true glacier ice until it lies about 300 feet below the
surface.

Hardly any melting occurs on the surface of the Antarctic ice sheet. The major thing that causes it to diminish is

the calving of icebergs at the seacoast. The ice sheet most likely began when the ice sheets of West and East Antarctica, two regions that are geologically quite different, joined together. These original ice sheets were themselves probably formed by the merger of various ice caps high in the mountains. (The dates for these events are being eagerly sought.) Inland some ice may be as much as three miles thick but it thins as it moves out toward the edges of the continent. In East Antarctica the inland ice can flow directly into the sea, sometimes forming large ice tongues in front of glaciers. In West Antarctica, the region of our travel, the passage of the inland ice to the sea is often blocked by many very high mountains and the ice must move between them in the form of enormous glaciers. Our flight to the Pole was partly over the Beardmore Glacier, once thought to be the largest on the continent. The Beardmore and many other spectacular glaciers are created by the Trans-Antarctic Mountains which slow down the advance of the South Polar Plateau. These glaciers do, however, give a great amount of ice to the Ross Ice Shelf, but it gets its largest increment from Marie Byrd Land, whose mountains do not create as much hindrance. The Ross Ice Shelf in West Antarctica is the largest such feature in the world, but the Filchner Ice Shelf in the Weddell Sea is not much smaller and, in fact, turns out to be larger with each new exploration. Ice shelves can create enormous icebergs. One berg was discovered that had the same area as the state of Connecticut.

The inland ice sheets are so high that they seem to make the Antarctic the loftiest continent in the world. It is calculated, however, that if it were ice-free it would be about the same elevation as other continents. Inland, the Antarctic is practically a desert with an average snowfall of only five or six inches, which works out at less than an inch of water. (The average rainfall in New York City is 42 inches, that in Phoenix, Arizona, is 7 inches.) The ice sheet maintains its size and even grows, however, because the sub-zero temperatures inhibit evaporation.

Far inland the ice is flat and featureless. The area is relatively windless and the ice is sufficiently thick to absorb stresses that might alter it. Toward the sea, however, there are winds called katabatic winds that flow gustily downhill under the force of gravity. Katabatic winds carry snow along in blizzards that pile it up in dunes known as sastrugi. These winds flow most strongly down the steepest slopes and a knowledgeable explorer can tell a good bit about the terrain by looking at the sastrugi.

The most obvious features of ice sheets are crevasses. These are nothing more than great cracks caused when ice is tortured to the breaking point. Crevasses are very common in glaciers, but they can also be discovered on ice shelves. They can be as much as 100 feet wide but are seldom more than 300 feet deep, not bottomless as they are often described in fiction, but quite deep enough to give trouble to a vehicle or even a man on foot. Crevasses are not seen very often deep inland except around low outcrops of rocks known as nunataks. The inland ice sheet has surface changes actually too small to be conventionally observed. Detected by instruments, these are differences in elevation that are caused by bedrock far below the surface.

As has been said, surveys during the IGY greatly increased the estimated amount of Antarctic ice. If even more water is tied up there than had previously been supposed, then it becomes even more important to find out whether it is growing or getting smaller. One way to find out is to measure the amount of snow accumulation and balance this by the amount that is wasted into the sea by icebergs. A simple way to measure accumulation is to dig pits in the snow to depths of eight or ten feet and measure the annual snow rings. This is usually possible because summer snow is softer, more coarse, and less dense than winter snow. Numerous snow pits have been dug at South Pole and Byrd Stations as well as a great many more at locations widely distributed over the ice sheet. It seems certain that the amount of snow, and thus the ice, is increasing. After many observations and calculations of the calving of icebergs, scientists concluded in 1965 that the net amount of Antarctic ice was increasing. This does not quite square with the observation that the sea level around the world was increasing slightly every year. To explain this apparent contradiction, scientists suggested that ocean water was expanding due to the recent general warming of the climate. Measurements of the Antarctic ice budget will certainly continue. The trends observed at present are too short-term to provide solid conclusions.

One additional way to determine the ice budget is to find out how fast the ice sheet is moving. Satisfactory methods for doing this have not yet been completely worked out, but it is presently estimated that it would take tens of thousands of years at least for a snow flake that fell near the Pole of Inaccessibility to reach the edge of the East Antarctic ice sheet.

Considerable evidence supports the idea that at some time in the past the ice sheet was considerably thicker and broader than it is at present. Scratched rock surfaces above the present level and exposed boulders that have obviously been transported from some other place both point to this. Moraines (hills of debris left by retreating ice), ice-free valleys, raised beaches that were formerly coastal areas now uplifted after the removed of ice pressure, and the discovery of moraines on the sea floor some distance out from the edge of the present ice sheet, all demonstrate a bigger mass of ice in the past. That the ice has retreated seems most obvious at the coast but exposed mountains far inland also show distinct evidence of glacial activity hundreds of feet above the present level. When did this larger ice sheet begin to decline? Some researchers have tried to fit it in with the disappearance of the North American ice sheet and date it neatly at about 11,000 years ago. Evidence for this convenient idea is lacking at the moment. Maps, photographs, and botanical and glacial observations taken during the last fifty years show that the edge of the ice is either stationary or retreating at a very slow rate.

At least one prominent glaciologist, Anthony J. Gow, doubts that the North American ice age bears much relation to the situation in the Antarctic. He observes that the northern ice sheets were very active and delicately adjusted to climate changes. The Antarctic ice sheet does not seem to have been disturbed by global climate changes because it has its own internal or "glacially induced" climate that insulates it from the violent changes suffered by glaciers elsewhere. The Antarctic ice sheet is much colder than it needs to be to sustain itself and Gow expects it to remain constant as long as the world's present geography exists. This conclusion does not keep Dr. Gow or others from continuing to investigate the world's greatest sheet of ice.

Of all the scientists involved in glaciology, those from the U.S.S.R. have been particularly interested, perhaps in part because of their experience with the Arctic Ocean that borders their northern shores. The Russians have been especially concerned with the cause or causes of ice ages. They have a large population living within the Arctic Circle who would be among the very first to feel the effect of a new ice invasion. Some of their men agree with the theory of the Americans Ewing and Donn, who proposed that ice ages in the north come about when the Arctic Ocean becomes free of ice and prevailing winds can pick up its moisture and dump this as snow on the lands just to the south. As the snow accumulates and becomes thick ice, it presses outward and moves south, overcoming all obstacles in its path. The growing ice cap lowers the sea level so that the Gulf Stream, which has been entering the Arctic seas and warming them, is no longer able to flow into the area. The Arctic Ocean then begins to freeze over and the prevailing winds can no longer pick up its moisture to create snow. The ice sheet, no longer nourished, begins to melt in the summer sun and the ice recedes. The Russians who agree with this idea only complain that it should be credited to a Russian sea captain, E. S. Gernet, who first proposed it in 1930.

Russian glaciologists working in the Antarctic have been very open about their work and have supplied Western scientists with numerous papers written to describe their projects. One of their papers discusses the thought that polar ice caps do not owe their existence to changes in climate but that the climate itself is due to the existence of ice caps. The Russians have done a great deal of work on the problem of producing more and more accurate ice budgets. One major study has been on the observed increase in temperature (and thus the intensification of atmospheric circulation), that has increased the snow accumulation at various Russian and U.S. stations. This study finds that snowfall, as observed by pits dug below the surface, has actually increased in recent years. Another study has concerned local recessions in ice sheets that have been shown at a number of places. Attempts have been made to improve the quality of snowfall measurements and to find some way of determining the annual total discharge of icebergs in the sea. A Russian, Milankovitch, has attempted to improve the theory that says ice ages come about because of changes in the axis of the earth's rotation. Studies in the causes in sea-level fluctuation are being made, particularly those that may come about when ice caps reflect less heat from the sun due to the increased amount of dust in the atmosphere. Some Russians have also tried to find scientific support for the ice age theory of a New Zealander named Wilson who suggested that ice ages come about when the Antarctic suddenly becomes so engorged with ice that it deposits not just icebergs as big as Connecticut into the sea but masses of ice that are continental in size. These masses are so large that they take many years to melt, meanwhile making the entire world so much colder that new ice caps develop even as far away as the Arctic Ocean. (Wilson suggests that these Antarctic cataclysms occur about once every 70,000 years.) One Russian paper reassuringly concludes about the ice budget that the Antarctic is so cold and so vast that even the very noticeable planetary warming trend of the twentieth century has had no effect upon it.

Less cosmically, in recent years, Russian scientists have reported on their analysis of brine in ice shelves (does the Ross Sea freeze from the bottom after all?), their attempts to predict sudden breaks in ice shelves and the behavior of ice in Mirny harbor (of very practical importance at their major supply base), and on their attempts to understand the laws that govern the routes taken by icebergs. For this they have tagged icebergs with barrels with requests inside asking the finder to report where he had discovered the drifting berg. They have also worked on a theory of glaciers, on an understanding of how the microscopic living things called diatoms weaken the ice in which they are frozen, and the physical laws that operate in the process of crevasse formation. At their inland stations the Russians are experimenting on ways of drilling through the deep ice by means of heat. These are all certainly peaceful projects that demonstrate a very real interest in knowledge for its own sake. Glaciologists of the U.S.S.R. and the U.S. regularly exchange information and often individual scientists as well. A new ice age or a rising sea level is of equal importance to both nations.

Although current U.S. research into glaciology is conducted mainly at Byrd Station, it is not confined only to that point. The ice at McMurdo Sound is studied scientifically, and practically, so that it can be properly utilized for aircraft, travel, the hauling of freight, and the loading and unloading of ships. Part of this involves ice forecasting, almost as involved as predicting the weather. To help in the work, the sea ice is mapped regularly using the data from satellite photographs. For glaciology, the South Pole station is now used experimentally for just one project, a new technique to melt deep holes in the ice by means of a suspended heating element. A wire in attached instrument package sends data on the temperature and density of the ice back to the surface. The visitors flying down to the Pole did not go just to see this one project, but the trip made glaciers and the Antarctic ice cap not just so many words or ideas but very real and physical matters.

CHAPTER III

TO THE SOUTH POLE FOR LUNCH

THANK you, Arville Schaleben. An editor on the *Milwaukee Journal*, one of our press group, he had seen clearly at six-thirty in the morning that I was not rising for breakfast. Since our little bus was due to leave for the ice airport at seven-thirty, he very thoughtfully brought me an orange and a doughnut from the mess hall so I would not starve during the 800-mile flight to the South Pole. Thanks to Arville, all I had to do was get into my complicated cold-weather gear and climb aboard our transportation. Being shaven was neither required nor even expected.

Our plane was the same Hercules we had flown down in from New Zealand, with the same crew. Two admirals were aboard, the one in charge, Rear Admiral David F. Welch, and a visiting one, Rear Admiral Paul E. Seufer. Also with us were four lady geologists from Ohio State and the scientist–wife of a New Zealand biologist whose mission was to study the penguins on Ross Island.

Soon after an easy take-off at a sunny eight in the morning, I asked co-pilot Lieutenant Commander Campbell how soon we would reach the Beardmore Glacier. He glanced at a chart and said "About thirty-five minutes." Even more than the Pole, this is what I wanted to see on the trip. Named by Ernest Shackleton, who discovered it in 1908, for an English industrialist who helped finance his expedition, Beardmore Glacier has a number of claims to fame. It is one of the largest in the world, about 140 miles long and in some places 40 miles across, hemmed in on both sides by high peaks of the Trans-Antarctic Range. Crevassed and treacherous as this great river of ice is, Shackleton and his men used it as their path from sea level to the Ross Ice Shelf (which it helps feed) to its top, above 10,000 feet, where it stops and the central Polar Plateau begins. Shackleton got to less than 200 miles from the Pole when he had to turn back because food was running out. Three years later, Robert F. Scott used the same dangerous route, because even crevasses are not quite as bad as climbing directly over the high mountains. Scott did reach the Pole but he and his men died on the way back of starvation—blocked by a blizzard only eleven miles away from the next supply base. In 1968, from a tent base near the head of the Beardmore Glacier and only 325 miles from the Pole. Peter Barrett climbed a rocky mount about a half-mile high above the ice and came upon the remains of his labyrinthodont, his animal fossil. The Beardmore Glacier has became the standard route for planes on their way to the Pole. From photographs I had seen I knew it must be as beautiful, in a terrible way, as anything one could find on this earth.

Thirty minutes after questioning the co-pilot I went up to the flight deck, full of anticipation about the great sight I expected. We were at 30,000 feet and below us there was nothing but thick clouds. Commander Campbell shrugged his shoulders in apology, and I returned disappointed to my seat, stumbling over a number of sleeping fellow passengers as I did so. For the remainder of the trip there was nothing one could expect to see. Just the incredible white expanse known as the Polar Plateau. Snow and ice clear to the horizon and usually about two miles thick. I remembered a classic line I had read: "Antarctic flying consists of hours of sheer boredom, interrupted by moments of stark terror."

Then we began to descend and touched down exactly on time, at eleven o'clock. Three hours from McMurdo Sound. It had taken the first man who ever got there, Roald Amundsen, traveling by dog sled, almost two months to make the trip.

When the plane had come to a halt (with the engines still running, as they would during the entire time of our stay), we looked out our windows with great curiosity. Then the big cargo door at the rear was lowered and the male passengers stepped out onto the snow. Then Admiral Welch, with the six ladies all arm in arm, walked down the ramp to the South Pole. There was to be no first among them. All arrived simultaneously. After much camera clicking, everyone well covered-up but removing their gloves to snap the shutters, we all began to walk up a very mild incline to the symbol itself, a barber pole set up at the exact geographical location. (Actually the true pole was now a half-mile away, the great ice sheet having moved that much since the barber pole was erected, but we all agreed we were close enough to say we were truly there.)

There was a mild wind, nine knots, and it was 49 degrees below zero, but these were minor matters. We had been warned about the altitude, well over 9000 feet, and it was this that made the little hill somewhat difficult to manage.

We had been advised to breathe deeply, to get enough
oxygen, but this was not easy in such cold air. Then the
nostrils began to drip and the sunglasses to fog up. After
a few minutes more of photographing at the barber pole,
everyone seemed quite willing to climb down some steps
into the Pole Station itself. Charles Neider, one of our
press group, had already gone below. One of the men who
came out to welcome us had ordered him to do so. He
was getting frostbite, which could be seen at the tip of his
nose. At first Charles was indignant about being ordered
about and asked "Who are you?" The man replied mildly,
"I'm the doctor here." So Charles obeyed.

But, before going below, I paused for a good, unhurried
look at the phenomenon I had flown half-way around the
world to see. Robert Scott had called it the most God-
forsaken place in all the world. It may very well be that,
but it has a quite awesome beauty at the same time. On
the brilliantly clear, sunny day of our visit I could see,
squinting even behind my glasses, clear to the edge of the
horizon in every direction, a vast expanse of absolutely flat
snow and ice, the absolute white tinted slightly gold by
the sun almost exactly overhead. The only relief in the
scene was our airplane and an outline of some of the roofs
of the Pole Station not yet completely submerged under
the snow. I had the impression that if I simply walked to
the horizon I would find a clear drop-off and the end of
the world. It was easy to see here why some people continue to insist that the world is flat. At the exact bottom
of it, the world looked that way.

The U.S. installation at the South Geographic Pole was
formally dedicated on January 23, 1957, and named the
Amundsen-Scott Station. Officially it is 9184 feet above
sea level and rests on a base of ice at least two miles thick,

a sheet of ice so heavy that it has depressed the land underneath it a thousand feet or more. Eighteen U.S. scientists and Navy men wintered over at the station during its first year, the first people ever to live there. It was built almost entirely by equipment supplied from the air, and aircraft flights are its present only means of support. The cost of all this may be understood in terms of the value of gasoline by the time it has been delivered to the South Pole. At this point it is worth $6.50 per gallon.

The average temperature is −56.7 degrees Fahrenheit. The lowest ever recorded was −113.3 degrees and the highest was 5.5 degrees above zero. One of the constructions at the South Pole Station is a sauna, a steam bath, where the temperature reaches about 210 degrees. In 1958 this sauna provided the inspiration for an organization that is probably unique. It is the "250 Club." To qualify for membership an applicant must first become superheated in the bath, then run outdoors naked to roll in the snow, then very quickly and vigorously dry himself. It must be at least 40 below outside to achieve the necessary 250-point spread. Some hardy men have managed to stay as long as fifteen minutes before fleeing back indoors for comfort and safety. The record point spread is 278 degrees. None of the visitors with whom I traveled asked to join the club.

We were greeted most cordially in the station's lounge by the scientific leader, Frank Merrem, a specialist in the physics of the ionosphere, and by the Navy officer in charge, Lieutenant Dean Fadden. These two men, with assistance from some of the other scientists, gave us a briefing on the logistics of the station itself and the research work being carried on there. (During the summer there would be thirteen scientists in residence. Six of them would stay on during the long, dark winter when the only communication with the rest of the world would be by radio.)

As mentioned, the housing at the Pole was designed to last for only a few years, but it has been continuously occupied since its completion. Originally it was built on the surface of the ice, but slowly it has gone more and more underground, covered by drifting snow. The increasing weight of this snow has been crushing the buildings, making some of them useless. Others were saved for a time in 1963 by the addition of supporting arches to keep the roofs from caving in. A one-tenth scale model of a new station a half-mile from the present location has now been set up. The new one, it is hoped, because of its design, will stay above ground and not become buried as the snow drifts. (There is very little snowfall on the Polar Plateau, but since the snow never melts it continues to accumulate.)

What was so worthwhile about the barren South Pole that made it seem desirable to establish a base there at a very great cost? Originally, the U.S. Government was moved in part by considerations of national prestige. The U.S.S.R. had announced as part of their plans for the International Geophysical Year the establishment of two permanent bases in the Antarctic. The United States decided that it had to at least match this effort, and the audacious idea of a permanent base at the Pole came into being. The mere challenge of doing such an impossible thing, in a place where no man had stood for more than forty years, excited the official imagination. Then the impossible was accomplished.

Somewhat minor side-effects of its existence was that it could serve as a way-station for parties making overland traverses of the continent, a use made of it by the parties of Vivian Fuchs and Sir Edmund Hillary, and as a fueling stop for aircraft making long reconnaissance flights into very inaccessible areas of the vast land.

Scientifically, Mr. Merrem told us, the Pole Station has a number of varied uses today. It has the unique quality of being one of the two places on earth that are absolutely stationary, relative to the sky directly overhead. Thus it is a very valuable base from which to observe the skies above. Continuous observations can be taken at the same point on the celestial sphere.

The Pole is also valuable as a weather station, radioing daily reports to McMurdo as one unit in the continental meteorological network. The Antarctic in general is remarkably free from seismic activity, earthquakes; the Pole, cushioned by thousands of feet of ice from the rocks below, is an excellent location for seismometers, the instruments that detect activity within the earth's crust. It is part of a world-wide earthquake watch, and any unusual activity is immediately radioed to Washington, where the information is used to help pinpoint the earthquake's location. This is also part of the tsunami warning system, an international network of particular value to countries bordering the Pacific Ocean where tsunamis, popularly called tidal waves, created by earthquakes, have caused great devastation in coastal areas. Lastly, we were told about upper atmosphere physics, the most important research at the Pole (a subject we were to learn more about later) and then we adjourned for lunch and talk on a more informal level. I was most curious to hear about the effects on human beings of long periods of isolation, months of it without a sight of the sun. One fact I had heard of before was that most men arrived with great amounts of books, to catch up on their reading, but that very little reading was actually done. Curiously, there seemed to be little or no gambling. The men do have some movies, of course, tapes of music, and a number of hobbies, but most of them seem to spend unusually long hours at their work, and this is their major recreation. In summer, of course, there are aircraft in and out almost every day, but the winters are a true test of character. As far as I could tell, no one seems to have ever had a serious mental breakdown. Since wintering there is purely voluntary, the men arrive knowing what they may expect.

Our visit to the South Pole lasted only two hours. We had been told, even before leaving the States, that the trip was a chancy thing and that we might not ever get there at all. No one could guarantee good flying weather or good radio communications or that something might not happen which would make an aircraft unavailable. That was why the long trip was scheduled for our first day on the ice, right after the 2300-mile trip from New Zealand. A day of rest at McMurdo might have been nice but instead we went to the Pole as soon as possible. If it had to be cancelled on that first day, there was still a possibility that it could be rescheduled before we had to leave.

Goodbyes and thank-yous were brief at 49 degrees below outside the housing and we all hurried down to our waiting plane, whose engines had been running all during our visit. Perhaps the length of our stay was determined by the amount of gasoline we were consuming. And, as it was, the pilots and crew were putting in a good long day on our behalf.

Take-off was uneventful and, seasoned Antarctic travelers now, we soon settled down for the bland three-hour trip to McMurdo. It was not, however, to be quite like that.

About an hour out, co-pilot Campbell told me that the sky was clear now above the Beardmore Glacier and the word spread quickly among the passengers. Getting out my map, I calculated when we should reach it and was one of the first tourists up on the flight deck. Soon others followed, all with loaded cameras. There we learned some fairly sensational news. Ordinarily the Hercules cruises most economically at 30,000 feet, but the Admiral had ordered a very special treat. He ordered the pilot to take the ship down and cruise at only 300 feet above the ice. For spectacular sightseeing from the air, such a trip cannot be improved upon anywhere. (We learned later that this is only done about once a year. It is not only costly but at least a little bit dangerous.)

Leaving the white monotony of the Polar Plateau we were rapidly approaching the black peaks of the central Trans-Antarctic Mountains. Here the massive ice sheet from the interior flows slowly but inexorably around the high stone barriers and through the valleys where it re-forms into the rivers of ice known as glaciers that descend by force of gravity from fields as high as 10,000 feet downwards to the sea where, in this area, they mostly feed the great barrier known as the Ross Ice Shelf. There are quite a number of these glaciers but the Beardmore seems among the most awesome.

Flying down the glacier toward McMurdo, the valley is flanked on the left by the solid wall of the Queen Maud Range and on the right by the peaks of the Queen Alexandra Range. It was hard to think of these stark mountains as fossil country.

The broad windows of the pilots' cabin offered an

excellent panorama. It seemed as if more people had crowded in there to get a look at the magnificent view than strict regulations might allow, but I imagine the friendly pilots did not want to deny anybody their full appreciation of what must be one of the most spectacular sights in the world.

Looking straight down, the ice we were rushing past at several hundred miles an hour was not white but blue and green, indicating that it was very, very old, perhaps many thousands of years. We were keeping pretty much in the center of the glacier, away from the peaks on both sides now high above us, and here the ice was twisted in a maze of deep crevasses each of which must have been hundreds of feet deep. It seemed completely impassable to anyone on foot and I wondered what we could do if we had to crash here. It was very beautiful and strange and might easily have been terrifying.

Yet Ernest Shackleton had climbed this glacier in 1908 and Robert Scott had followed him three years later. That men, without dogs, could have dragged heavy sleds past all this, in extremely cold weather, up to such high altitudes seemed unbelievable. Then I saw the only way it could have been accomplished. Toward the edges of the glacier the ice was not as tortured. For certain distances it almost seemed smooth.

Looking at the great mountains flanking our sea of ice, I wondered how a man selects the one he wants to go geologizing in. In the late afternoon light, for twenty miles away, they all looked equally black, lifeless, and menacing. Of course, by now many geologists have tramped among them, taking samples, comparing them, determining their age and their ancient history. To the scientists they are not just great, remote, inaccessible hunks of stone but textbooks in which they can read the past. And, as the fossils have proved, they were not always lifeless.

At last, satiated, I struggled my way out of the crowded cabin and returned to my seat. I tried to write down some observations, some brilliant words that would immortalize my experience, but my vocabulary was not up to it. (Someone recently asked me, "What was the Antarctic really like?" and I felt temporarily speechless. It can be described, up to a point, and there are thousands of great photographs, but, like some physical sensations, no one can tell you. Nothing can match the physical experience itself.)

Our entire trip down Beardmore took less than half an hour. (It had taken the first explorers weeks to climb it.) The rest of the trip could only be an anticlimax. Some time over the featureless Ross Ice Shelf, another glimpse of Mount Erebus still smoking faithfully, and down very smoothly at Williams Field. We visitors had only been "on the ice" about twenty-four hours but, once you have been to the South Pole, it is not hard to feel like a very experienced hand.

We took the familiar bus to our quarters, selected our dinner from the excellent variety offered at the cafeteria, and moved on to the Officer's Club. Here I found myself becoming a little irrepressible and anxious to tell whoever would listen about our great adventure. There I learned how exceptionally lucky we had been. Many, if not most people, who come down here never get to the Pole. What is more, our special Beardmore trip was highly unusual. To my surprise, I found our news was greeted with a certain amount of envy.

But everyone wanted to know about Jim Kroth, and I

could do nothing to enlighten them. None of our party knew it, but Kroth had been supposed to return from the Pole aboard our plane. A meteorologist for the Weather Bureau, he had spent a whole year down there, wintering over, of course, and then he had missed the plane! This news seemed appalling to everyone. How was it possible?

Then a very bright-eyed, apple-cheeked, ebullient young man more or less bounded into the room. Here was Jim Kroth himself, and he was greeted with cheers. What had happened? Well, he had been told the plane was leaving at two and he was still making the rounds at the Pole Station, saying goodbye to old friends, when the plane took off at one, as scheduled. Fortunately, another plane had come in for fuel two hours later and he hitched a ride to McMurdo. A happy ending to what could have been a very sad tale.

At exactly eight o'clock the morning following our trip to the South Pole, we took off from the McMurdo ice once again to see Byrd Station, the other U.S. scientific village deep within the Antarctic. All the material for the original housing and labs, built for the IGY, had been brought overland by snow trains from the makeshift seaport, at the edge of the Ross Ice Shelf, called Little America V. Byrd Station was 450 miles away from the water and could be reached on the ground only through the heavily crevassed area around the Rockefeller Mountains. The men who built it did so only after months of incredibly dangerous and difficult work. It went into commission just three weeks before the Pole Station, on January 1, 1957. Within three years it became clear that the structures erected on the surface could not survive the weight of much more snow accumulation on their roofs, and a new underground base was built, six miles away, consisting of eight man-made trenches covered with steel arches overhead. Only some ventilators, scientific equipment, and some summer support facilities appear above ground. It is now completely supplied by air from McMurdo Sound, more than 800 miles away.

With the luck of our trip the sun was bright and the weather clear but there was little we could expect to see during the 800-mile, three-hour trip but the vast white sheets below called the Ross Ice Shelf and the Rockefeller Plateau. No Beardmore Glaciers today. I did, however, learn that the Polar Plateau is not quite as featureless as it is generally supposed to be. Pilots have found enormous crevasses at some places on its surface that seem to remain stable for years. These have been given names like Steer's Head and Big Bertha, usually for their shapes, their positions have been fixed, and the fliers use them for visual sightings. Our Hercules crew were the same efficient men we had had the day before. Fewer passengers this trip. No lady scientists, but fortunately the ever-interested, ever-cheerful Jean Pearson of the *Detroit News,* a very young lieutenant commander, with a very fancy piece of photo equipment, on inspection tour to study construction problems, the commanding admiral's flag lieutenant, and the two admirals themselves.

During the flight to Byrd, I learned that Admiral Welch had already been down here remarkably early in the season. Except for radio communication, Byrd Station had been absolutely cut off from the rest of the world since the previous February 15. Then, late in August, a message came through telling of a medical emergency. The station has a doctor who winters over, of course, but one of the sailors had developed diabetes and such complicated abdominal problems that the M.D. on hand had neither the equipment nor the medications needed to handle the emergency. Two Hercules were dispatched from Quonset Point, Rhode Island, where the squadron winters over, and made the long flight down to McMurdo by way of New Zealand. Taking advantage of the opportunity, the aircraft carried seven scientists to McMurdo, plus food and mail, and Admiral Welch, who took this opportunity for a look at his very unusual command. One Hercules went on to Byrd, with the Admiral aboard, making the flight without incident and landing in 29 below zero temperature with a wind of twenty-eight miles per hour. What made this unusual was that the landing had to be done in the darkness. The Hercules unloaded its food and mail for the isolated men, and the sick sailor was safely evacuated. Then the plane returned to McMurdo, picked up its companion plane, and the two craft made the long 2300-mile flight over ice and water to New Zealand and conventional daylight.

Five such winter medical evacuations have been done since the first Hercules came to the Antarctic (one, a Soviet exchange scientist from Byrd), but obviously it is a rare event. After the mercy flight, Byrd was isolated again until October 20, just a few weeks before our trip there.

Statistically, Byrd Station does not seem as forbidding as the South Pole. It is only 5000 feet above sea level instead of 9000. Its average temperature is only a −18 degrees F. And, once, on January 31, 1961, it had a record high of only 2 degrees below freezing. When we landed there it was just 30 below. The specially designed clothing is so good that the main effect of the cold, if you do not stay out too long, is that your nose runs and your breath makes your sunglasses fog up. Still, walking a quarter

mile or so from the aircraft to the ramp that leads down
forty feet into the base is something of an effort. Unlike
the Pole, the land is not absolutely flat and there is a decided incline up to the entrance. It was fresh and clear
and exciting, however, and the crunch of the bunny boots
on the crisp snow had a satisfying sound. Of course, it was
only relative, but Byrd Station seemed more welcoming.
Perhaps, even this rapidly, I was becoming used to the
atmosphere of the Antarctic. It has been frequently said
that man is the most adaptable of all animals. And certainly no other animal has succeeded in living on the
Polar Plateau.

But why should man go to so much effort to adapt
himself to a place such as this? Our scientific and Navy
hosts seemed happy to explain as we gathered in the
general club room after a long walk through the ice-
walled tunnels. (The tunnels are kept cold so that the
heat from the living quarters will not melt the ice all
around and above. These corridors are also the refrigera-
tors, of course.)

The major project in glaciology at Byrd Station is the
deep drilling into the ice sheet. This great mass is important to scientists because of all the frozen history it contains. Over the ages all sorts of matter have fallen on it,
along with the snow, and this material has been buried
in the succeeding years. Pollen, dust, volcanic ash, tiny
meteorites, and tektites from outer space are all contained
at various levels beneath the surface. Study should provide clues to the events that caused these particles to be
in the atmosphere, but, most importantly, the cores should
show the past history of weather and tell how old the ice
really is.

The drilling at Byrd began in 1957 when a conventional

oil rig dug a hole somewhat deeper than 1000 feet, before the limit of the apparatus was reached. This old hole is still being studied to see how parts of the ice sheet at various depths are moving in relation to each other, but the hole is gradually closing up. In the season of 1967–68, a new drill was brought to Byrd, one that had been tested successfully in Greenland to depths around 4000 feet. On January 29, 1968, the new drill reached the bottom of the ice at a depth of 7100 feet. The bottom turned out to be covered by a thin film of fresh water, about 30 centimeters thick. The researchers hoped to core the bottom rock itself, to find out what the great ice sheet rested on, but they were unsuccessful. About half-way to the bottom the drill ran across ice that was many degrees below zero, but from there on down it began to warm and at the bottom it was estimated to be just a few degrees less than freezing. Anthony Gow, one of the scientists in charge of the project, believes that the ice warms up near the base because of heat flow from the earth itself (what the researchers call geothermal activity), but friction of the moving ice sheet may also contribute a bit to the heat observed.

The core from this record drilling through ice was recovered ninety-nine percent intact. Half the total length of the core was flown to McMurdo Station, taken aboard the U.S. Navy ship *Wyandot,* then stored in a refrigerator while the ship sailed to Davisville, Rhode Island. There it was met by refrigerator truck which carried it to cold-storage facilities near the U.S. Army Cold Regions Research and Engineering Laboratory at Hanover, New Hampshire. This organization, usually referred to as CRREL, is a major American study center for glaciology.

Preliminary analysis of the mile-and-a-half core showed

bits of granite near the base. The report on this subject mentions that the nearest exposed granite from Byrd Station appears in the Whitmore Mountains, more than 200 miles away. (It should be mentioned that the entire ice sheet is in constant but very slow motion, and the lower sections move more rapidly than those near the surface.) Several layers of dirt and volcanic ash were found. There are a number of volcanoes, no longer active, less than 200 miles from Byrd. The volcanic debris found at depths between 4000 and 5000 feet was estimated to have fallen on the surface 15,000 to 35,000 years ago. Ice from the bottom of the core could be as much as 50,000 years old. The deep hole from which the core was taken has been filled with fuels to prevent it from refreezing and closing so that it can be used for other studies. For several seasons Swiss scientists have tested a technique of water-dating they developed that hopefully will give the age of the ice by dating the radioactive carbon it contains.

Future plans call for a truly international drilling project. French, English, Russian, and American scientists will work together to bore a hole somewhere in East Antarctica where the ice is much colder and thicker than it is at Byrd Station. The researchers are looking for the oldest ice they can possibly find, and East Antarctica near the Russian Vostok Station seems the most likely area. A new drilling rig is being devised for this program that ideally will overcome the mechanical problems caused by the unusual kind of mineral known as ice.

Although not a Byrd Station project, it was there that we learned about a new technique, still in the early stages of development, that should help men overcome problems created by the great ice sheet. In this project, ice is not seen as a source of knowledge but a great cover that conceals the continent underneath. To find out what lies below the white blanket, radar is used as the probing instrument. Radio waves of suitable frequency can be used to penetrate ice, unless the ice is partially melted, in which case it becomes a poor conductor. Ice sounding radars have been developed in the United States, Russia, and at the Scott Polar Research Institute in Cambridge, England. The first one was tried out in the Antarctic by Russians who carried it over the ice in a vehicle. This broke through a crevasse, killing the driver and injuring two engineers. The British tried a similar operation from their camp at Halley Bay in Queen Maud Land. Three men were killed in a crevasse on that attempt, and the records of a previous journey were lost. The British have now developed an airborne radar that records the ice depths on film. The radar is carried aboard a Hercules aircraft operated by the U.S. Navy. Initial tests penetrated deep into the ice and showed a profile of the mountains and valleys that were invisible. The airborne record is continuous, in contrast to the widely spaced depths found by seismic shooting. The seismic method requires that explosive charges be set off every few miles, the depth of the ice being determined by the length of time required for the sound of the explosion to reach bedrock and return to the surface. Seismic shooting was not only spotty but very dangerous and slow. When the profile of the Antarctic is drawn by radar it will be reproduced on maps so that navigators in the air can simply turn on their own radar sets, get a picture of the land beneath them and check this visually with the pictures that have already been published. Ideally, finding your way over the vast Antarctic ice sheet would become as simple as it is for a driver to use a road map. Before this goal is reached, however, many flights will have to be made to discover the landmarks and these will have to be located by very accurate navigational fixes. (In the 1920s, pilots like Charles A. Lindbergh flew the mail by following railroad tracks and the courses of rivers.)

Our visit to Byrd Station lasted more than an hour longer than had been planned because the visitors, including Admiral Welch, were so interested in hearing about the ice research and other scientific work there that they did not want to leave. It was fortunate that the Admiral was along because it required someone of his rank to alter the Navy's rigid schedules. We had time for lunch. Then time was even found for a brief tour underground. We saw the drilling equipment, some cores, the tunnel where the fuel (aviation gas and Diesel) is stored in rubber bags that can hold thousands of gallons apiece. The capacity for storage is 150,000 barrels and the previous winter the station had used 130,000 barrels. As at the Pole, the cost of fuel at Byrd is reckoned at $6.50 per gallon delivered.

Finally, we learned a few details of living here. Every day someone must go above to shovel drifting snow off the escape hatches. Fire is a constant worry in the Antarctic and these hatches must be kept open. The water detail was another point of interest. Every man, no matter what his rank or job, has one day in which he must shovel enough snow down a chute to a melting plant to produce the 1600 gallons of water the base uses every day. It takes four gallons of snow to produce one gallon of water. The job is made somewhat easier in that a bulldozer pushes the snow up to the opening of the chute but it still has to be shoveled down by hand. It usually takes a man a full day to complete his work. On leaving I asked Mr. Evans Paschal, the scientific leader, if it was this water detail that

kept him looking so trim. He said it was not that, but that
he could not stay underground all the time without getting
claustrophobia. Some men, he continued, were happy to
stay underground all the time, when they could, but his
laboratory was five-eighths of a mile away and he walked
there every morning, returned to the base for lunch,
walked back again, and then returned in time for dinner.
I asked about blizzards and the long dark nights. He replied that he had a line strung along which he could
guide himself, but admitted that some times he omitted
returning for lunch and simply had a sandwich in his lab.

CHAPTER IV

THE MYSTERIOUS ELECTRIC
ENVELOPE

Every nation involved in the Antarctic has sent men there to probe the mysterious envelope surrounding the world that is called the ionosphere. Their various studies are usually classified under the general name of upper atmosphere physics. This is a branch of study quite as modern, as exotic, and as abstruse as nuclear physics. Except for the Northern and Southern Lights, the auroras that we can see, human beings have no sensory equipment to tell them that, high above the blanket of air surrounding the earth, there is a region full of violent electrical activity.

The auroras were the first upper atmospheric phenomenon to attract speculation because they were so visible. The explorer Captain Scott, by no means a physicist, wrote very poetically about the aurora australis. "It is the language of mystic signs and portents. The eastern sky was massed with swaying auroral light. Fold on fold, the arches and curtains of vibrating luminosity rose and spread across the sky. The brighter light seemed to flow, now to mass itself in wreathing folds in one quarter from which lustrous streamers shot upward, and now to run in waves. The appeal is to the imagination by the suggestion of something wholly spiritual, something instinct with fluttering ethereal life. One wonders why history does not tell us af aurora worshipers."

Later visitors to the polar regions sought more down-to-earth explanations for the existence of these wild lights. Many theories exist, but so far no one has been able to synthesize a completely accepted theory of cause and effect. The auroras seem to occur when particles from the solar wind collide with the earth's magnetic field. The solar particles caught in this field are drawn toward the polar ends of the magnet, and, as the magnetic lines at the poles are closer together, they pass through the atmosphere. At this level solar particles may collide with air molecules and the collision releases some of the particles' energy as the lights called auroras.

The Japanese and the Russians are particularly active in aurora work. The U.S. stations at Byrd, South Pole, and McMurdo also make numerous studies because the auroras are most visible at high latitudes near the Poles. The best way of finding out about the lights is simply to look at them. This could be tedious, inexact, and physically quite miserable during the long winter nights when they are most obvious, so most of the looking is done by all-sky cameras that can take pictures that scan from horizon to horizon. There are various kinds of cameras in use, and all take color films because the color variations are one of the mysteries. Auroras also vary in shape, in intensity, from day to day and from one season to another. (Auroras in the Antarctic tend to be much fainter in color than their northern counterparts.) It has been found that they are much more intense, not at the geographical Poles, but near the magnetic ones. Attempts have been made to show that displays of Northern and Southern Lights occur simultaneously, due to some excitation of the ionosphere, but that they happen at opposite ends of the world at the same time has been very hard to prove. For one thing, when one polar area is in darkness, the time when the lights can be most easily seen, the other polar area is in constant daylight. Auroras may occur during the day but this has been very difficult to demonstrate. Moreover, they may not even be confined to the polar areas at all. A faint auroral display has often been observed at an astronomical observatory in Africa. The fact that auroras are most commonly observed at the polar ends of the world does seem to indicate that they are *somehow* related to magnetic activity since it is at the ends of the planet that the magnetic field comes closest to the earth's surface.

This matter of the invisible magnetic field around the earth was made most clear to the journalists by the scientific leader at Byrd Station. He seemed almost too young to hold a position of executive responsibility, but actually a scientific leader does not exercise authority in the military manner; he functions mostly as a diplomat between the Navy and the scientists who tend to be somewhat individualistic. The Antarctic being full of men with beards and long hair, this scientist expressed his personality by keeping his head completely shaven, as if he were bald.

His specialty was the physics of the atmosphere, the study of interactions between the earth's air envelope, the geomagnetic field that the earth radiates, and the radiation that comes to the earth from the sun and space. Another major object of the study is to understand the

behavior of radio waves. In the Antarctic studies are made
of the aurora and airglow, VLF (very low frequency)
radio noises such as "whistler" and "hiss," how radio waves
are propagated, the extent to which the ionosphere absorbs energy from the sun, cosmic ray bombardment, and
fluctuations in the earth's geomagnetism.

The earth's atmosphere extends out far beyond the point
where it can support human life. The most distant part of
the atmosphere is not empty, however. A constant stream
of charged particles keeps arriving in this region, full of
tremendous energy. The particles from the sun, known
as the solar wind, travel at speeds of 250 miles per second,
spreading the sun's magnetic field through the space between the planets. When this wind strikes the earth's magnetic field around the Van Allen Belt, a battle goes on to
see which will dominate.

This struggle is most obvious in the auroras. They occur
mostly in polar regions, he believes, because the earth is
like an enormous bar magnet with its ends in the Arctic
and Antarctic. Energy particles from the sun, caught in
the earth's magnetic field, are deflected along the lines of
force that connect the ends of the magnet. Around the
Poles, the lines of force come close together, pass through
the atmosphere and the particles from the sun descend
to a point where they can collide with molecules of air.
Some of the energy from this collision may be released as
light, the auroras.

Auroras are much more common in some polar areas
than in others. Byrd Station is such an area and it has a
conjugate point, the Great Whale River in Canada, where
auroras may occur almost simultaneously. The phenomenon is studied at both points at the same time.

Another Antarctic study concerns airglow, a condition

not completely understood, in which a barely visible light fills the night sky. It is thought to be caused by chemical processes that occur when the upper atmosphere relaxes from the effects produced by sunlight during the day. If so, what produces airglow during the long polar night?

VLF radio phenomena are studied at Byrd because it is remote from man-made radio disturbance. VLF "whistlers" come when strokes of lightning send out radio waves that bounce back and forth along the geomagnetic lines of force between conjugate points. In a radio receiver they sound like a series of whistles with a regularly descending pitch. "Hiss" may come from man-made signals that also run along the geomagnetic lines. The mechanics of these events and the source of energy are not yet known although many ideas have been suggested.

A very major feature of Byrd Station is the long-line antenna, actually 21 miles long, that is designed to transmit very low frequency radio waves. Radio waves are reflected off the ionosphere, the electrically conductive layer of the upper atmosphere. Long distance radio communications depend on its ability to reflect, particularly in the lower levels. The lower levels of the ionosphere, the "D" region, are the reason the radio reception is better at night than during the day. When high energy particles from the sun penetrate to that region, it absorbs (rather than reflects) more radio waves of medium and high frequency, the frequency range of commercial radio stations. During the night the particles do not enter the "D" region and radio signals penetrate to higher levels before being reflected back to earth. This extremely long antenna receives signals from various parts of the United States, from the Canal Zone, and from England. Studies are made on how they vary, depending on normal daily and seasonal changes and on various kinds of disturbances in the ionosphere. Receivers such as this one cannot be used on solid ground because they are too inefficient. This long antenna is much more effective because it lies on top of more than 8000 feet of ice, a poor conductor of electricity. It was built thirteen miles away from Byrd Station to avoid any interference from Byrd's generators or from other radio equipment.

As at all U.S. Antarctic stations, the mysterious form of energy known as cosmic rays, particles that bombard the earth from somewhere outside our solar system, are studied intensively at Byrd. All polar stations are good receivers of cosmic rays because the earth's magnetic shield forces them into these areas. Cosmic rays vary in intensity, and understanding the reason for this may eventually provide a clue to their origin.

Operating Byrd Station is a very expensive proposition and, to some people, year-long duty there is a hardship. Plans are now underway to see whether all, or most, of the observations now taken of events in the upper atmosphere, and weather observations as well, cannot be automated. Prototype machines are being tested for their reliability and to see whether they can survive the atrocious climate. Machines can obviously do some jobs better than men, but there are people who maintain that the brain of an active human being is in many ways still necessary. The Byrd experiment in automation is just one of many reflecting this argument. (The difference in opinion among experts is most publicly apparent in the question of whether or not manned space flights are necessary.)

Back at McMurdo, the visitors from the news media were introduced to other researchers working in ionosphere projects. One morning we knocked on the door of a small house about a mile away from the station. It was occupied by Bill Trabusco, a cosmic ray man. He had wintered over and was just about to be relieved to return home. I fear we woke him up, but he was very gracious and soon had coffee ready. Trabusco had meant to read seriously during the winter season but, as seems to be the case with all men in the Antarctic who have this intention, he did not do so. Instead, he remodeled the house. He built a combination bar and lunch counter, and re-covered the walls and ceiling using materials he found in a Navy warehouse. He did not mind the darkness. In fact it was not usually truly dark, the moon and the stars providing light most of the time. Concerning the lack of mail he was quite philosophical. When you get mail, he said, you get all shook up. When you know you can't get it, you don't worry. His house was considered a field party by the NSF because it was one mile away from the base. To keep fit he often walked to and from town, though he could have phoned for a vehicle. One amusement he found was his short-wave radio. With it he accidentally tuned the frequency on which the crew of the Apollo 11 communicated with the earth and he listened to their conversations direct. He had spent a total of $70 during his thirteen-month stay.

Officially his work was described as "a long-term project to measure variations in cosmic ray intensity that occur minute-to-minute and year-to-year and correlate them with findings from a world-wide cosmic ray network. Under this project, new knowledge about the magnetic fields in space and new insight into the solar system, our galaxy, and cosmos should be gained."

As Trabusco described it, cosmic rays are ninety percent

high-velocity protons, charges of energy that come mostly from outside the galaxy, though some are created by solar flares. They are detected on earth by tubes similar to TV tubes and also by Geiger counters. These receivers are geared so that only high-energy particles will trigger them. The receiving station in the Antarctic is there because cosmic rays are deflected by the earth's magnetic field and drawn to the magnetic poles. It is not necessary to go to the magnetic pole itself, however. The signals are sufficiently strong at McMurdo. (The house, naturally, is away from town to avoid local radio interference.) Trabusco prepared weekly reports on cosmic ray activity after his computer had analyzed the data, as part of the worldwide network. The cosmic ray receivers might be left unattended and only observed from time to time but there is a lack of confidence that they will always be working correctly and so a man who can fix them is always on hand. Trabusco is a physicist, but he learned to repair the instruments after a course that took several months. Cosmic rays from beyond the sun take only sixteen minutes to pass through the solar system. The sun knocks them off their original course. Are they dangerous? No, only solar rays are dangerous to the earth. As we left I was glad to realize that cosmic rays could be so simple.

Our next stop was a cottage named Great Hill House at the summit of Crater Hill. Here our host was Chris Shepherd who called himself an OAE, or Old Antarctic Explorer, because this was the second year he had wintered over. The previous tour of duty had been spent photographing auroras at Byrd Station. Why do people come back? "I guess it's the beauty of the place." As a result of his stint at Byrd, Shepherd wrote a scientific paper called "Auroral Absorption Occurrence Patterns as a Function of Magnetic Activity."

Officially, his station is known as the Riometer Site. This stands for Relative Ionosphere Opacitometer. His instruments measure the resistance of the ionosphere, the envelope of electrically charged particles that surrounds the earth, to radio waves. His receiver listens to the background radio noises that come from the galaxy and beyond. Ordinarily the receiver, which prints its records on a slowly rotating roll of paper, shows very little change in this noise. When a solar flare occurs, though, the record changes wildly. A crippling radio blackout begins, particularly in polar areas, very soon after the surface of the sun bursts a flare that sends high-energy waves hurtling out into space, including the space around the earth. The earth's own magnetic field prevents the waves from entering the earth's ionosphere where the belt is thickest, around the equator, but the solar particles are drawn toward the magnetic poles, disrupting the ionosphere and thus blacking out radio signals. The solar flare itself is brief but the ionosphere takes days to calm down again. Solar flares are closely watched at McMurdo and the other stations. With compasses useless because of the nearness of the South Magnetic Pole, with few visual aids to help a pilot over what is usually a trackless expanse of ice as far as the eye can see, navigation by aircraft without radio assistance is too difficult and dangerous to be done except in emergencies.

A very unusual solar flare had stopped all radio communications just a few days before our arrival. To predict such blackouts, the sun is studied every day with telescopes and spectrometers from a Government station in Boulder, Colorado, to spot any unusual activity. The recent flare had not been expected, though the activity had been observed, because the center of the disturbance was moving around to the far side of the sun, not observable from earth, and the chances of its having any effect on the earth were about two percent. There have only been three flares of such size since 1960. Flares only take twenty-eight minutes to reach the vicinity of the earth. Shepherd had seen it coming, but there was no time to send a warning before the McMurdo radio was blacked out from the rest of the world.

Mr. Shepherd, a plasma physicist employed by the McDonnell Douglas Company, explained why his firm is interested in solar flares. They are the prime contractors for the Apollo spacecraft that fly to the moon. Any one of the three great solar flares that have happened since 1960 could have killed the astronauts or at least prevented any communication with them. One large expense of the spaceships is the heavy shielding needed to protect the passengers. The weight of the material used to keep them from being bombarded by high-energy particles is a major factor in the amount of power needed to launch the vehicle. If solar flares could be predicted, moon voyages with much lighter craft could be made when solar flares were unlikely. The Riometer Site at McMurdo is only part of a network called the Space Disturbance Forecast. There is another site at McMurdo's conjugate (or opposite side of the earth) point, Shepherd Bay, an inlet of Hudson Bay.

The small house which is the Riometer Site lies in a very attractive location. Through a picture window the occupant can gaze down at Scott Base, Williams Field, McMurdo Sound, and the distant mountains across the ice. Going outside he can stare up at Mount Erebus, twenty miles away but seeming much closer. Shepherd admitted that he had taken the job in part because he had seen the house on his previous stay and he had wanted to live in it. He said he was not the least bit lonely, but if he were, there was always his pet skua bird which comes every day exactly at noon to be fed.

Pleasant as this visit was, we had to move on to the Geodetic * Satellite Lab run by Dave Smith. It too was comfortable, but had no view as spectacular as the Riometer's. What goes on in it, however, would have been inconceivable a few years ago. From here, and from similar sites around the world, the shape of the earth is being determined, and the earth is not pear-shaped as we have been told. This station and another like it at Thule in Greenland are tracking Navy navigational satellites that circle the earth in polar orbit. There are five such satellites in the sky at present. As they pass overhead they transmit radio signals to the ground to receivers such as the one at McMurdo. These receivers measure the Doppler effect, which changes as the satellites' orbits change. The orbits vary because they are affected by the earth's gravitational pull, a pull that differs because the earth is not one constant size nor of uniform density. Smith showed us a photograph of a globe of the earth constructed on the basis of six years' reading of information from satellites. The official name of the globe is "The Geoid as Determined by Doppler Tracking of APL Satellites." It shows that the earth is not an oblate spheroid, as has also been suggested. The earth as depicted here looks somewhat lumpy with variations of many feet in the sea level. Satellite geodesy may soon change a number of textbooks.

* Geodesy is the science of determining the size and shape of the earth and the gravity field associated with it.

CHAPTER V

ORDEALS OF THE HEROES
(1902 TO 1917)

THE life of the scientists and the Navy supporting force today in the Antarctic, though hardly luxurious,
is certainly not one of physical hardship. To give visitors
a contrasting sense of what men went through during the
"age of heroes," the Navy provides a tour of three historic
huts built by the parties of Robert Scott and Ernest
Shackleton in the first decade of this century. Because of
the extreme dryness of the environment, they are remarkably well preserved. The first one, erected by Captain
Robert Scott's British exploring group in 1902 for the
international "Antarctic Year," was right at McMurdo
Station itself.

Scott's expedition, aboard the *Discovery*, arrived on
February 7, 1902. The hut, really a pre-fab, had been built
in Australia to serve as quarters for the party wintering
over, but Scott felt that the *Discovery* could safely be
frozen in for the season and the men could live aboard
the ship. Nevertheless, the hut was erected close to the
ship on a small bare plateau of volcanic rubble. Construction was hindered by the difficulty the men found in dig-

ging holes for supports in the permanently frozen ground.

Scott wrote, "The main hut is of most imposing dimensions and would accommodate a very large party, but on
account of its size and the necessity of economising coal
it is very difficult to keep a working temperature inside;
consequently it has not been available for some of the
purposes for which we hoped to use it. One of the most
important of these was the drying of clothes; for a long
time the interior was hung with undergarments which had
been washed on board, but all these water-sodden articles
became sheets of ice, which only dried as the ice slowly
evaporated. When it was found that this process took a
fortnight or three weeks the idea was abandoned.

"But although the hut has not fulfilled expectation in
this respect it is in constant use for other purposes. After
the sledging it came in handy for drying the furs, tents,
etc.; then it was devoted to the skinning of birds for a
month or more ... finally it has been used both for the
rehearsal and performance of such entertainments as have
served to lighten the monotony of our routine, and in this
capacity, when fitted with a stage, footlights, etc., it probably forms the most pretentious theater that has ever been
seen in polar regions. ...

"In the midst of these vast ice-solitudes and under the
frowning desolation of the hills, the ship, the hut, the busy
figures passing to and fro, and the various other forms of
human activity are extraordinarily impressive. How strange
it all seems! For countless ages the great somber mountains
about us have loomed through the gloomy polar night with
never an eye to mark their grandeur, and for countless ages
the wind-swept snow has drifted over these great deserts
with never a footprint to break its white surface; for one
brief moment the eternal solitude is broken by a hive of

human insects; for one brief moment they settle, eat, sleep, trample, and gaze, then they must be gone, and all must be surrendered to the desolation of the ages."

(Scott was certainly correct about man's insignificance in the vast land but wrong about the "human insects" surrendering. A small town now exists right next to his old hut, full of busy people without time or inclination to be in awe of their surroundings. On our tour of the town I heard one sailor ask another, "How's your love life?" Under the circumstances, a pretty funny remark.)

The other huts at Cape Royds and Cape Evans are only a brief helicopter ride away. These early visitors had the attainment of the South Pole as their major objective, but Scott, in particular, also had numerous scientific programs. He brought along geologists, "physiographists," physicists, and surveyors. During his two visits five years of meteorological, magnetic, and tidal observations were made. While sailing in on the Ross Sea his men took ocean soundings from the deeps to the continental shelf, bottom samples, and water temperatures from various layers. They studied icebergs and sea ice and also observed whales, seals, penguins, birds, and fish with great interest. Scott was particularly concerned with getting emperor penguin eggs at various stages of development to find out what he might about the birds' evolutionary history. During his stay he sent out exploring parties. One found wood fossils, the first evidence of such material in the Antarctic. Another party discovered one of the strange dry valleys that exist between some of the mountains a hundred miles or more across McMurdo Sound.

Scott made his first attempt on the Pole from Hut Point. He had a point of view about getting there that seems particularly English and sentimental. He had dogs with

him but did not really believe in their use for polar exploration and, in particular, did not care for the idea of killing his sledge dogs and eating them after they had outlived
their usefulness. (Peary, who successfully reached the
North Pole, and Amundsen, first man to achieve the South
Pole, both followed this practice.) Scott decided he would
use human traction, three men in harness pulling a sledge
with a tent and all their provisions. Scott was stubborn
and refused all the advice given him about the usefulness
of dogs, believing that the use of human beings as beasts
of burden "makes the conquest more nobly and splendidly
won."

Scott had another blind spot as well, this one relating to
the dietary disease known as scurvy. Scurvy, whose symptoms include general ill-health, sallow skin, loss of energy,
anemia, great weakness, bleeding gums, foul breath,
loosening teeth, painful muscles, and bleeding beneath
the skin, results in death unless properly treated. On long
voyages without fresh food, ship crews often suffered
greatly from it; one British expedition lost 300 out of 500
men to it on a voyage around the globe. Then Captain
Cook showed that it could be avoided if the crew got
plenty of fresh fruits and vegetables. In time the Admiralty
doctors in London came to believe that scurvy could
simply be prevented by serving the men great amounts of
lime juice (hence the expression "limey" came to mean an
Englishman).

In time British crews began to realize that lime juice
was not enough and that other fresh fruits and vegetables
were needed also. The doctors persisted, however, and so
Scott's expedition was furnished with a great deal of lime
juice, plus canned and bottled fruits and vegetables. No
one paid any attention to the fact that the Norwegian,

Fridtjof Nansen, had wintered over in the Arctic, eating nothing but fresh seal meat, and had emerged without any symptoms of scurvy. Seals were abundant near Scott's base but he did not take much of their fresh meat with him when he, Ernest Shackleton, and Dr. Edward A. Wilson set out to make a deep penetration of the continent. They traveled 308 miles south over the frozen Ross Sea, but never reached land, and then they had to turn back, although still well provisioned, because all three suffered from scurvy to a greater or lesser degree. Shackleton was by far the most sick and had to be carried on a sledge for the last days of their three-month journey. The three men did manage to get back to Hut Point alive and slowly began to recover, but Shackleton was sent home. Scott wintered over for a second year during which he and his men made a great number of scientific observations.

During this second season Captain Scott and Dr. Wilson made the trip from Hut Point to Cape Royds to see penguins. Scott wrote in his diary, "When within a half mile of the open water, north of the sea ice, Wilson suddenly said 'There they are.' I looked and, lo and behold! On the dark bare rocks of Cape Royds there was a red smudge dotted with thousands of little black-and-white figures—a penguin rookery without a doubt. It is wonderful that we should have been here two years without knowing of this, and it is exasperating to think of the feasts of eggs we have missed. . . ." The men made camp and Scott continues, "From our tent door we look out on to the open sea, deep blue but dotted with snowy-white pack-ice. Erebus towers high above us on our right, and at the left we look away over the long stretch of fast ice to the cloud capped western mountains. We hear the constant chatter of the penguins, and find a wonderful interest in watching their queer habits." The next day they were astounded to see two ships fighting their way south into McMurdo Sound. These were the *Morning* and the *Terra Nova*, sent to rescue them if necessary. Scott's ship *Discovery* was to be abandoned if still frozen in, but the pack ice broke out just in time and all three ships sailed to New Zealand together.

Back in England, Ernest Shackleton was under a cloud. Scott reported that the huge Irishman suffered a "physical collapse" and implied that, without Shackleton, his expedition could have gone much farther south. In addition to this blow to the Irish pride, Shackleton had been refused a commission in the English Navy and defeated in an election when he ran for Parliament. Then his luck turned. He had been working for a man named Beardmore and this rich industrialist agreed to finance a new expedition. Shackleton made his plans and announced them in the London *Times* on April 12, 1907. He would send one party to explore the unknown land east of McMurdo, another to the South Pole and a third to the South Magnetic Pole. Scott, then in command of a Naval vessel at Gibraltar, read the story and wrote Shackleton saying that he planned another expedition of his own and asking him not to use the building at Hut Point. Shackleton was stunned but agreed.

The explorer and his men aboard a small ship called the *Nimrod* arrived in McMurdo Sound in January 1908. The ice had not gone out as far as it had in 1902, and the *Nimrod* could not penetrate as far as Hut Point, even if Shackleton had decided to ignore Scott's request. His ship could get no further in than Cape Royds, where Scott had visited the penguins four years before. The ship was moored to the ice near the Cape on the night of February 3, 1908. A level site half a mile inland from the rookery, protected by a ridge that cut off some of the prevailing southern winds, was selected for the housing. Tents were erected for living ashore while the hut was being built. While four men chiseled through the bedrock right beneath the lava rubble, all the other hands moved to unload the ship. This was accomplished by February 22, and the *Nimrod* immediately sailed away, leaving fifteen men to survive through the winter.

The supplies brought ashore at Cape Royds in many respects did not differ much from those used at Hut Point. There was a large, insulated pre-fab house, boxes upon boxes full of food in tins and bottles, nine Siberian dogs, and fifteen Manchurian ponies. Shackleton, like Scott, had little faith in dogs. The Manchurian ponies had never been tried out at all under such conditions.

The great experiment of the expedition was an automobile. It was a 12–15 horsepower machine called an Arrol-Johnston. It was air-cooled, for water would have frozen. The carburetor was wrapped up and the exhaust thus recovered used to re-heat the engine. The car's frame was reinforced to withstand the temperature, special oil was used, but the fuel was plain gasoline. The engineer in charge was a man named Bernard Day. Shortly after unloading he announced to his impressed colleagues that tests would begin. No motorized vehicle had ever been used in either polar area. It began well enough, but then its wheels sank in the deep snow after a trip of 100 yards. A second try succeeded no better. On the third attempt the car went half a mile before stopping. It had to be pushed before it could return to camp. Shackleton would not give up so easily, however, and announced that, with the right wheels, it could run 95 miles per day. Bernard Day felt that the weight of the auto was the problem, so it was stripped down to a seat riding on a bare chassis. With matters thus arranged, the Arrol-Johnston was loaded with 750 pounds of supplies and took off to establish a depot at the foot of Mount Erebus miles away. Between 9:30 A.M. and 6:45 P.M. it did manage to get there and back. The temperature stood at 22 below zero. The work it had done would have taken six men two or three days. The automobile continued to be used with some success establishing depots until December 1, when it fell into a crevasse. It took two hours to set it free. This was the last journey for the car, and it was laid up when it returned to the hut. Although his attempt was not entirely successful, Shackleton was the first man to point the way to using motorized vehicles on the ice, the almost universal form of travel on the Antarctic ice today.

His party, always working out of Cape Royds, was quite successful in other ways. Two of his men were the first to climb Mount Erebus, a 13,350-foot peak, in temperatures of 22 below. They estimated that the crater was about 800 feet deep and half a mile across. A party of three, including the Australian Douglas Mawson, set out for the South Magnetic Pole on September 18, without dogs or ponies, hauling their 2200 pounds of equipment with breast harnesses. After an arduous journey full of great hardships, they reached the South Magnetic Pole and returned to Royds on February 4, 1909, a trip of 2400 miles. They came back with a tremendous number of scientific notes.

Shackleton saved the South Pole for himself. He had calculated the distance as a bit more than 800 miles and he planned that the trip coming and going would take ninety-one days. On October 29, 1908, he left the base with three companions. There were four sledges pulled by four ponies, the other ponies having died. Horses fell into crevasses, broke their legs, or died from exhaustion. On November 26 Shackleton had gone farther south than Scott; about the same time he realized that he would have to cross a 10,000-foot range to reach the Pole. Then he came upon an indentation he named the Beardmore Glacier, after his sponsor, and began the painful climb. The very last pony, Socks, was lost in one of the first Beardmore crevasses. As Shackleton wrote, "the loss of Socks, which represented so many pounds of meat, was a very severe blow for us, for we had after that to use sledging stores at the depots to make up for the lost meat. If we had been able to use Socks for food, I have no doubt we would have been able to get further south, perhaps even to the Pole itself."

Shackleton's narrative of the trip gives a vivid picture of the situation. "During the last weeks of the journey outward, and the long march back," according to one excerpt, "we really thought of little but food. The glory of the great mountains that towered high on either side, the majesty of the great glacier up which we travelled so painfully, did not appeal to our emotions to any great extent. Man becomes very primitive when he is hungry and short of food."

In his narrative Shackleton also says, "On the outward march we did not experience really severe hunger until we got on the great glacier, and then we were too much occupied with the heavy and dangerous climbing over the ice and crevices to talk much. Then on the plateau our faces were generally coated with ice, and the blizzard wind blowing from the south made unnecessary remarks out of the question. Those were silent days.

"It was on the march back that we talked freely of food,

after we had got down the glacier and were marching over the barrier surface. The wind was behind us, so the pulling was not very heavy, and as there were no crevices to fear we were able to keep close together. We could take turns in describing the things we would eat in the good days to come ... there was to be an anniversary dinner every year, at which we would be able to eat and eat and eat."

On January 9, within 110 miles of the Pole, Shackleton and his men had agreed to give up because, under the best possible conditions, they could not hope to return alive if they continued on from their present position. Not only were they almost starving, their clothing was falling apart, the winds were terrible, the altitude made work very difficult and gave them severe headaches, and the meat from the horse that died from exhaustion had given them dysentery. The utterly spent men reached base on February 28, 1909, after a trip of 117 days.

The Shackleton expedition had discovered 500 miles of new mountains, explored a great glacier, collected coal specimens and fossil plants, discovered the South Magnetic Pole, taken the first motion pictures, and brought the motorized vehicle to the Antarctic. The *Nimrod* was ready to sail when the South Pole party arrived, and they left the hut at Royds in such a hurry that later visitors found half-eaten rolls of bread, socks hanging on the line, and many other indications of a hasty departure. The *Nimrod* was anxious to leave. A fierce blizzard had been raging for days and the ship's captain wanted to get out during a lull in the storm.

If it were not for the weather, the site of the Cape Royds hut would be ideal for a tourist resort. Behind, the spectacular smoking Erebus, snow-covered, shining in the sun. Within a half-mile, several fresh-water lakes. Facing the sea, the penguin rookeries, and across the Sound, the great western mountains of the Society Range. At the foot of the hill, a beach. When the weather is warm the rookeries do smell highly of guana, however, and it is hard to say how this could be cleaned up without disturbing the birds.

Shackleton described the shack as "not a very spacious dwelling for the accommodation of fifteen persons, but our narrow quarters were warmer than if the hut had been larger. The coldest part of the house when we first lived in it was the floor." Cold air could circulate under it until the men closed it in. Everyone lived in the same room and each man built and decorated his bunk to suit his fancy. Some privacy was offered with canvas curtains. The only built-in room was Shackleton's, and he gave it up for the convalescence of a man named Brocklehurst whose feet had been badly frostbitten on the ascent of Erebus. Dr. Marshall had had to amputate one of his big toes (a "cradle" that elevated his injured foot can still be seen in the hut today). The dining table that accommodated fifteen people stood in the middle of the room. It had removable legs and could be hoisted to the ceiling between meals to get it out of the way. For recreation there were books and magazines, a good supply of records, cards, and other games. Two of the men, Joyce and Wild, knew something about printing and they produced a volume of original writing called *Aurora Australis* right in the hut. In many ways the hut was primitive, cold, and cramped. The plumbing was out of doors, the furniture was all made of packing cases, but a member of one of the field parties, after hard sledging to the south, described his impressions on returning to the place. "Delicious luxuriating in all the comforts of Antarctic civilization. . . . Oh! the luxury of a dry blanket after a stifling wet sleeping bag."

After its abandonment by Shackleton and his men, the Cape Royds hut stood alone in the wilderness, unobserved except by penguins, battered by the winds but standing firm, the wood of its construction and the contents inside almost intact due to the extreme dryness of the climate. Then, in 1911, men from Scott's new base at Cape Evans, eight miles closer to Hut Point, scrambled over the glacier to have a look. One of the visitors wrote, "The door of the porch had carried away, but the inner door was standing. We entered with much curiosity. We opened one window, and the place might have been abandoned the day before. On the low table in the center a meal had been left. Condensed milk, saucers, biscuits, jam and gingerbread. The latter were very good, and not harmed by exposure. At the back was a tray from the oven with a batch of scones, just cooked, and a loaf of bread. The 1907 expedition left in a hurry, I believe, which accounts for the somewhat unkempt appearance of the hut." The visitors found a bottle of gooseberries and another of currants. They had brought bacon and ship's biscuit with them. They also discovered plum pudding, sardines and Nestle's milk, as well as ginger, raisins, and corned beef. They drank currant and gooseberry vinegar, along with all the other things, and decided that "Antarctica is immune from dyspepsia, for we felt none the worse." Other parties visited Royds in the years immediately following, some out of curiosity but others in search of stores left behind that might be useful in other camps. In one situation, the men were low on matches and delighted to discover a whole case that lit perfectly after many years.

Then Cape Royds lay neglected until the modern era of

Antarctic exploration. Admiral Dufek, leader of the first Operation Deep Freeze, declared that all the old huts near McMurdo would be considered shrines and left untouched. In 1960, a New Zealand group went down to undertake whatever restoration might be necessary. Royd's major need was a new roof. Many of the things left behind in 1909 have disappeared but quite a bit remains, including a cake of Lifebuoy soap, to show how the men lived. The restorers have put out a booklet available to the visitors who arrive, a few at a time, perhaps a few every week during the season. "You are privileged to visit the old huts in McMurdo Sound where great men of the 'Heroic Age' of Antarctic exploration once lived. As you enter these huts, please remember that you are on historic ground and pay the reverence due to the memory of those who toiled, suffered and, some of them, died to unlock the secrets of the Great White South.

"It is desired that these huts should be preserved as nearly as possible in their original condition, as lasting memorials of these pioneer explorers of the Antarctic. We need hardly remind you then, that any defacement of these memorials, or any pilfering of souvenirs from them would be gross vandalism."

Scott had been one of the first to greet Shackleton on the railway platform in London when the latter returned, successful in many respects but not in reaching the Pole. Shackleton could hardly raise another expedition very soon, and Scott saw that the coast was clear for him to make the ultimate discovery, to plant the English flag on the bottom of the earth before any other man could reach it.

On June 15, 1910, Scott set out from England aboard the *Terra Nova*, which also carried nineteen ponies, thirty-four Siberian dogs, forty-five sledges, and three caterpillar tractors. The Scott party was decidedly scientific.

It also included a motion picture cameraman. The plan was to explore the east and west ends of the Ross Sea, then make a dash to the Pole. When Scott's ship, the *Terra Nova*, arrived in Melbourne, Australia, he was displeased to receive a telegram from Roald Amundsen, a prominent Norwegian explorer who was supposed to be planning an expedition to the North Pole. The telegram from him read, BEG LEAVE TO INFORM YOU PROCEEDING ANTARCTICA.

While outfitting for this trip north, Amundsen heard the news that the American, Peary, had already reached the much-prized North Pole. Without telling a soul about his intentions, Amundsen sailed from Norway and landed his ship, the *Fram*, at the island of Madeira on September 9, 1910. There he told his crew that he planned to achieve the South Pole and from there he sent his telegram to Scott. Amundsen reached the Bay of Whales, where Admiral Byrd later built his bases, in January 1911, planning to winter over and head for the Pole at the beginning of the southern spring.

Scott sailed into the McMurdo Sound area during the same month. He found that the ice would not permit him as far south as his old base at Hut Point, but he could get closer than the hut at Cape Royds. He had the *Terra Nova* moor to the ice near there and began unloading the ship on January 4. At first he called the location the Skuary but soon changed it to Cape Evans, in honor of his second in command. The first cargo off the ship was the motor sledges. These worked well at first though they did sound like threshing machines. On January 8 the third sledge was lowered onto the ice and driven off, but before it had gone 200 yards the sledge crossed a soft patch of ice, broke through, and nothing remained but a big hole. When the ponies were unloaded they were tethered on a patch of snow so they could not eat sand and die, as four of Shackleton's had.

On the first day of landing Scott almost lost his photographer. Scott saw the event himself and wrote, "Some six or seven killer whales, old and young, were skirting the fast floe edge ahead of the ship; they seemed excited and dived rapidly, almost touching the floe. As we watched, they suddenly appeared astern, raising their snouts out of the water. Close to the water's edge lay the wire stern rope of the ship, and our two Eskimo dogs were tethered to this. I did not think of connecting the movements of the whales with this fact, and seeing them so close to the ship I shouted to Ponting. He seized his camera and ran towards the floe edge to get a close picture of the beasts, who had momentarily disappeared. The next moment the whole floe under him and the dogs heaved up and split into fragments.

"One could hear the booming noise as the whales rose under the ice and struck it with their backs. Whale after whale rose under the ice, rocking it fiercely; luckily Ponting kept his feet and was able to fly to security. By an extraordinary chance also, the splits had been made around and between the dogs, so that neither of them fell into the water. Then it was clear that the whales shared our astonishment for one after another their huge hideous heads shot vertically into the air through the cracks which they had made. As they reared them to a height of six or eight feet it was possible to see their tawny head markings, their small glistening eyes, and their terrible array of teeth—by far the largest and most terrifying in the world. There cannot be a doubt that they looked up to see what had happened to Ponting and the dogs."

The wintering-over party moved into the almost completed hut on January 17. It was much larger and warmer than Shackleton's at Royds. Apsley Cherry-Garrard, a young zoologist in the group, later wrote about the comfortable Cape Evans hut, "Whatever the conditions of darkness, cold and wind might be outside, there was comfort and warmth and good cheer within." By the time he wrote this Cherry-Garrard knew very well about the terrible ordeals many of the men moving in would suffer later but, of course, the hut itself was not to blame.

After a few days' rest from the labor of unloading and building the hut, most of the party of thirty-one went out into the field. A party of four geologists left for the Western Mountains, the peaks that beckoned across the bay. Scott and eleven others went south to lay depots for the polar trip. Lieutenant Campbell and a group of five sailed east toward King Edward VII Land where they were to go ashore and do some exploring. Aboard the *Terra Nova* they kept as close to the Ross Ice Shelf as they could and thus discovered Amundsen at the Bay of Whales, settled in and preparing to strike south. The *Terra Nova* immediately returned to Cape Evans with this news, news that naturally disturbed Captain Scott. Deciding to leave the east to the Norwegian, Scott sent Campbell and his men, without their ponies, by ship to Cape Adare to explore Victoria Land, the area of the continent nearest New Zealand. The ordeals through which the isolated Cape Adare party passed did not become known to anyone else for two years.

By the time winter set in the other field parties had returned to the hut at Cape Evans. Life was cheerful there. Scott wrote, "The interior seemed palatial, the light [acetylene lamps] resplendent, and the comfort luxurious." Cherry-Garrard described the winter routine. "A sizzling on the fire and a smell of porridge and fried seal liver heralded breakfast, which was at eight a.m. in theory and a good deal later in practice. A sleepy eye might see the meteorologist stumping out (Simpson always stumped) to change the records in his magnetic cave and visit his instruments on the Hill. Twenty minutes later he would be back, as often as not covered with drift and his wind helmet all iced up. Meanwhile, the more hardy ones were washing; that is, they rubbed themselves, all shivering, with snow, of a minus temperature, and pretended they liked it."

Even though he was obsessed with the idea of being the first man at the Pole, Scott saw to it that the many scientific objectives of the expedition were pursued.

During his first expedition Scott had investigated the emperor penguin rookery at Cape Crozier on the far end of Ross Island but he did this during the comparatively mild summer. To him "it seemed probable that we have here the nearest approach to a primitive form, not only of a penguin but of a bird." Scott wanted studies made of the emperors while they were nesting but this was most difficult because, as has been said, they nest in winter. Their rookery at Cape Crozier, even in a straight line at least seventy miles away, was very difficult to get to by traveling over unknown territory in the darkness.

Nevertheless, Dr. Wilson, Lieutenant H. R. Bowers, and Cherry-Garrard set forth to visit the penguin rookery at Cape Crozier and bring back eggs in various stages of development. Their trip was appalling. Far from traveling in a straight line, they had to travel twice the distance detouring around crevasses. Temperatures went down to 77 below and they had only a tent for shelter. Once at Cape Crozier they built a sort of igloo that had rock walls and canvas for a roof. Their tent disappeared in a gale and so did the canvas roof of their igloo. For one day and a night they lay in their sleeping bags, otherwise unprotected from a blizzard. Somehow, they found their tent again and set off for the hut at Cape Evans, Cherry-Garrard carrying the total booty, three eggs and some skins.

Only July 1 Scott wrote, "One begins to wonder what the Cape Crozier party is doing. It has been away for five weeks." Then on August 1 at 10 in the evening, the three men appeared at the door of the Cape Evans hut. Cherry-Garrard staggered in first, his face mask completely frosted over, large icicles like bird's beaks sticking out from his lips. Scott thought he had never seen men so battered by the weather. "Their faces were scarred and wrinkled, their eyes dull, their hands whitened and creased with the constant exposure to damp and cold. That men should wander forth in the depth of a Polar night to face the most dismal cold and the fiercest gales in darkness is something new; that they should have persisted in this effort in spite of every adversity for five full weeks is heroic." Scott called this "the worst journey in the world" and Cherry-Garrard took the phrase for the title of a book. In it, back in England, he wrote, "I do believe anybody on earth has a worse time than an Emperor penguin." He also remarked, "Polar exploration is at once the cleanest and most isolated way of having a bad time that has been devised."

Apart from a few mishaps (a meteorologist had a very badly frostbitten hand as a result of getting lost while checking his instruments, the cook, while modeling for

the photographer, fell off an iceberg and was so injured
that he could do no more work, and a man named Griffith
Taylor, while trying out a bicycle on the ice, went so far
that a rescue party had to be sent out), life at Cape Evans
was a happy one, according to Scott. "I am very much
impressed with the extraordinary and general cordiality
of the relations which exist among our people. I do not
suppose that a statement of the real truth, namely, that
there is no friction at all, will be credited—it is so generally
thought that the many rubs of such a life as this are quietly
and purposely sunk into oblivion. With me there is no
need to draw a veil; there is nothing to cover ... If good
will and happy fellowship count towards success, very
surely we shall deserve to succeed." Alas for poor Scott,
the Antarctic is not an English gentleman but pure nature,
severe and without heart or mind. No reward is offered for
courage. If temporary conquests are made in this dire
region, they are only the result of competence.

Scott left his base on November 1, 1911. In the lead
were two ponies. Two dog sledges and two tractors proceeded on their own. The tractors failed after five days
when some bearings burned out. At the foot of Beardmore,
the lost ponies were killed and eaten. Scott's sentiment
about dogs did not apply to ponies. Once beyond Beardmore, Scott sent Lieutenant Evans and his supporting
party back, adding Petty Officer Edgar Evans from the
support group to his own. The party of five then carried on
south, hauling their sledges behind them. Lieutenant
Evans later gave his opinion of taking a fifth man. "Our
organization—tents, rations, equipment—was built on a
four man basis. Scott found that it took a half an hour
longer to cook for a fifth man."

On January 16, 1912, more than two months out, Scott's

party saw a black spot that stood out among all the immense white. It was Amundsen's tent and the South Pole that Amundsen had reached one month before. After three days of rest, a severely disappointed Scott ordered the return trip. He wrote in his journal, "I wonder if we can do it." When they reached the head of Beardmore, they stopped to gather thirty-three pounds of rock for the geologists, even though this added greatly to the weight of their sleds. Part way down the glacier Petty Officer Evans collapsed and died a few hours later. Soon thereafter, Lawrence Oates, his feet badly infected with gangrene, lurched out of the tent after saying, "I am just going outside and may be some time." He never returned, the surmise being that he gave his life to save the three men remaining. On March 21 the decimated party was out on the Ross Ice Shelf when they were stopped, eleven miles short of a depot, by a howling blizzard. They had fuel for one meal and provisions for two days. Huddled inside a tent, Scott made the last entry in his diary on March 29. "We shall stick it out to the end, but we are growing weaker, of course, and the end cannot be far. It seems a pity but I do not think I can write more." Then he added, "For God's sake look after our people."

Speculation went on for years about the cause of Scott's failure. Was it bad planning, bad luck, bad weather, or the man's romantic attitude toward his endeavor? Many people had their say but the people of the British Empire enshrined Scott as a hero. It is said they admire no one more than a gallant loser.

Long before Scott's fate was known to the men at Cape Evans, the *Terra Nova* had returned with mail and provisions. The ship had stopped at Cape Adare to move Campbell's Victoria Land exploring party to a new position

150 miles north of Ross Island. Nine men sailed for home in March 1912. Thirteen men remained behind to winter over. Parties led by Cherry-Garrard and by the surgeon, E. L. Atkinson, made journeys out to the ice to leave more provisions at the depots for Scott's party. On March 30, Atkinson left stores at Corner camp even though noting in his diary that he was "morally certain the party had perished." Scott made the last entry in his diary the day before, a hundred miles to the south.

The winter at Cape Evans passed without any great incident other than two fires, which were extinguished before severe damage was inflicted. In the spring, Atkinson, who had taken charge, debated whether he should try to rescue the Campbell party who might still be alive somewhere in Victoria Land or go south to see what had happened to Scott. The decision was to seek for Scott. On November 12 Atkinson's party came upon a tent. "Inside the tent were the bodies of Captain Scott, Doctor Wilson and Lieutenant Bowers. They had pitched their tent well and it withstood all the blizzards of an exceptionally hard winter." Then the discoverers removed all their personal effects, covered the men with the tent, and read the burial service. A cairn was erected above them and a cross made from two of their skis. (Gradually this shallow grave would be buried under the drifting snow and finally Scott and his men would be buried at sea as the Ross Ice Shelf moved north and met the water.)

Meanwhile, Campbell's Victoria Land party had returned to Cape Evans alive, though in a somewhat starved condition. Almost two years before they had been left at Cape Adare by the *Terra Nova*. There they built a hut and settled down to spend the winter. In the spring they carried out geological, meteorological, and biological work but could not get inland. The following spring the *Terra Nova* returned and took them south to a place they named Evans Cove. They were to be picked up again one month later. But the date arrived and went. The *Terra Nova* had been unable to get within twenty-five miles of land. The stranded but resourceful men cut their rations in half and began to kill seals and penguins to supplement their rations. By mid-April it was obvious that the ship would not return and they would have to spend the winter without provisions or any hut at all.

Somehow this group of two naval officers, a scientist, two petty officers, and a seaman managed to maintain a high state of morale and good humor in what might seem to be the world's most impossible situation. They dug a cave out of solid ice. It was nine feet by twelve feet, the size of an ordinary living-room rug, and only five and a half feet high. The men lived in it for six months. They killed all the seals they could find but were still half-starved. For nine months they neither washed nor changed their clothes. Then on September 30, 1912, about as soon as the sun came up, they set out for McMurdo Sound. En route they found several depots before they reached Cape Evans after a walk of about 260 miles.

Their appearance on November 7 brought a great deal of cheer to the men at the hut, depressed about the probable fate of Scott's group. The men who had returned from the apparent dead ate carefully at first, avoiding the troubles that often arise when a starving man comes upon abundant food. The *Terra Nova* arrived once more on January 18 and all hands worked so industriously to load everything needed aboard, including Scott's geological specimens, that the ship was ready to sail the next day. On January 20 the ship stopped at Hut Point so that the men could erect the cross to Scott at the top of Observaion Hill and then the *Terra Nova* steamed briskly back to New Zealand. It is doubtful that any of the party regretted the end of this expedition.

But, although the Scott party might be finished forever with the hut at Cape Evans, it had still another role to play in Antarctic history. If a person believed in such things, he might almost say there was a curse on the hut.

In 1915, Ernest Shackleton, thwarted in his attempt to be the first man at the South Pole, decided to try for another first. He would be the first man to make a crossing of the Antarctic continent. His route would be from the Antarctic peninsula south of South America across the vast sheet of ice to the Ross Sea south of New Zealand. Shackleton sent a party of New Zealanders, aboard the *Aurora*, to pioneer the final stage of his overland route and lay depots for him.

The *Aurora*, captained by Aeneas Mackintosh, reached Cape Evans on January 15. Ninety-eight cases of oil and ten tons of coal were landed. Then the ship moved south to Hut Point. From here sledging parties led by Captain Mackintosh and E. E. M. Joyce went farther south over the ice to set up the depots. A man named Stenhouse was left in charge of the *Aurora* during the Captain's absence. Stenhouse tried without success to find an anchorage near Hut Point and, failing this, sailed back to Cape Evans. Two weeks later a storm drove the ship thirty miles north, nearly crashing on the Barne Glacier as it passed. Two days later another storm drove the ship even farther away. It managed to return to Cape Evans, however. Two anchors were buried in the volcanic rubble on shore and the stern of the ship was attached to these anchors by six hawsers and a cable. The bow was also secured by anchors and the ship was all set to freeze in for the winter.

After these arrangements were made, four of the party went ashore to settle in at the old hut, carry out scientific observations and kill seals for food and fuel. They took no spare clothing with them and little in the way of food. At eleven in the evening on the sixth of May the wind was coming from the south and blowing at forty miles an hour. At three the following morning the men ashore looked to sea and found that the ship had disappeared! The lines to the anchors had all snapped. The stranded men kept a lookout for the *Aurora*'s return but were hampered by an extraordinarily fierce blizzard.

Six men of the party were still somewhere out on the ice, on depot-laying missions. Captain Mackintosh and his party of two got back as far as Hut Point on March 25 and found the other party of three lodged there. They could not return immediately to Cape Evans because the sea ice had not yet formed. The six lived in very miserable conditions at Hut Point until midnight on June 2, when they decided the ice was strong enough to support them. The depot-laying parties had lost all their dogs during their missions, but they were greeted noisily by the six dogs remaining at Cape Evans. To their horror, the *Aurora* was nowhere in sight.

The ten abandoned men faced an extremely critical situation. The tons of coal had been washed out on the ice along with the ship. There was food enough for the time being, but, Captain Mackintosh wrote in his diary, "The shortage of clothing is our principal problem. The members of the party from Hut Point have the clothes we wore when we left the ship on January 25 [three months before]. We have been without a wash all that time. We have been attempting to get a wash ever since we came back, but owing to the blow during the last two days no opportunity has offered."

E. E. M. Clark noted, "Clothing, there is none. The party just returned must still exist in their blubber saturated garments until we do some scouting ... we raised a quantity of canvas, several old sleeping bags, a bundle of old socks, parts of pony rugs, parts of old cookers, old Primus lamps, three old tents and poles, some old leather, three sailmaker's palms and needles, twine, etc. but no books, underclothing or Burberry's." These finds were the debris left behind by the Scott party.

The sailors in the party, Joyce and Wild, made rudimentary clothing from scraps of leather and canvas, from extra sleeping bags and, finally, from seal skins. All the men kept busy and every seal they spotted was killed to provide enough meat to keep them healthy and blubber to keep them warm. They were surviving but in a minimal sort of way.

They felt sure they could find additional stores at Shackleton's Cape Royds hut. Finally, in August, several of them crossed the sea ice to make the eight-mile trip. They found soap but very little tobacco. Seaman Wild, after experiment, produced a usable substitute, a blend of tea, coffee, sawdust, and a variety of herbs, and this became the regular smoke. They rationed the small amount of coal remaining because the sooty fumes from burning seal blubber made the entire hut greasy and black.

At last, on August 22, winter was over and Captain Mackintosh recorded the event. "The morning broke clear and fine. Over Erebus the sun's rays peeped through the massed cumulus and produced the most gorgeous cloud effects. The light made us all blink and at the same time caused the greatest exuberance of spirits. We felt like men released from prison. I stood outside the hut and looked at the truly wonderful scenery all around. The West Mountains were superb in their wild grandeur. The whole outline of peaks, some eighty or ninety miles distant, showed up, stencilled in delicate contrast to the sky line. The immense ice-slopes shone white as alabaster against dark shadows. The sky to the west over the mountains was clear, except for low lying banks at the foot of the slopes round about Mount Discovery. Then Erebus commenced to emit volumes of smoke, which rose hundreds of feet and trailed away."

With the coming of spring, the men felt they must continue their depot laying. With absolutely no communication, they could not know that Shackleton had never even landed on the continent, that his ship had become icebound in the Weddell Sea. The explorer would be looking for the depot planned to be the one farthest south, at the foot of Beardmore Glacier. Nine of the ten men set out, with only three tents, two in very poor condition, and three Primus lamps, old and without spare parts. [These were used for cooking.] Their clothing made the trip seem almost suicidal. All most of them had for trousers were made of canvas and they could expect temperatures between 10 and 60 degrees below zero. Leaving one man behind who was suffering from a frostbitten heel, the group set out for Hut Point on September 1. They had four dogs that still could be used. The motor sledge soon broke down and was abandoned. After much moving of material forward, step by step, some of the men did reach Mount Hope at the foot of Beardmore, in accordance with Shackleton's instructions. On the return the Reverend

Spencer-Smith died of scurvy and, before they reached Hut Point, Captain Mackintosh and V. H. Hayward along with Spencer-Smith's body were being dragged on sledges by the three men still able to walk and by the four dogs. The five managed to get to Hut Point on March 18. Here they were immobilized because the sea ice was not yet hard enough for them to make the rest of the journey back to Cape Evans. The inaction became too great a burden for Captain Mackintosh and Hayward, and the two set out on the ice on May 18 to make their way back. They were never seen again.

The rest of the men at Hut Point returned to Cape Evans safely on July 15. A few days after their return R. W. Richards collapsed and died, apparently the victim of a heart attack brought on by the strain of the long journey.

Of the seven men remaining two fell ill and the task of hunting seals for meat and blubber had to be carried out by the remaining five. In the spring they made another trip to Cape Royds, in hopes of finding provisions, reasoning intelligently if very unhappily that they might have to spend still another winter marooned at the end of the world. But then, on January 3, 1917, the *Aurora* was sighted, eight miles away across the ice. The men took their dogs and sledged in a great hurry to join it.

Everyone aboard was very happy to see them and eager to know how they had managed to exist. Of course the survivors were absolutely filthy and the rescuers were amazed to learn they had had no change of clothes in two years. Baths were prepared, clean clothes provided, and the men from Cape Evans at last began to feel somewhat civilized. Then they learned that the *Aurora*, after being driven off the shore to which it had been anchored, had been caught in the pack ice and drifted for ten months until it could free itself to return to New Zealand. By then it was too late to come back to rescue them and the mission had to wait until the 1916–17 season. Shackleton was aboard the *Aurora* on this rescue journey and he told them of his own ordeal. His ship had been caught in similar ice in the Weddell Sea and drifted for many months before it was crushed by the breakup of the floe. The misery that he and his men went through before they reached safety was at least as terrible as that suffered by the men at Cape Evans.*

For thirty years after these events, no human being disturbed the fierce tranquillity of the huts on McMurdo Sound. The blizzards raged unnoticed, the penguins, the skuas, and the seals pursued the life patterns that their ancestors had followed for millennia. Then, in February 1947, the icebreaker *Burton Island,* part of the U.S. Task Force for "Operation Highjump," penetrated McMurdo Sound and sent a party ashore by boat to have a look at the Cape Evans hut. They found it full of snow and could not go inside. It seemed somewhat unkempt after thirty years. Seal carcasses lay about, the frozen carcass of a dog stood on four legs as if it were alive, and numerous cartons of provisions lay about. A box of matches lit easily. A Navy helicopter that flew to Hut Point found it in much better condition. It looked as if it was abandoned a few weeks, rather than many years before. Newspapers and magazines lay around and some biscuits that were sampled were still edible, if tasteless. The following year a helicopter from the U.S.S. *Edisto* landed at Cape

---

* Shackleton's adventures on this expedition are beyond the scope of this book, but an excellent account of them is given in *Endurance,* written by Alfred Lansing and published by Avon Books, New York.

Royds and found it very well preserved. There was not much inside it, due to the foraging parties of the men marooned at Cape Evans, but the snow had not managed to force its way into this hut. When reconnaissance for Operation Deep Freeze began in December 1955, Cape Royds was considered as the site for a permanent land airport, but drilling revealed that it was not actually land at all. Under a two- or three-foot layer of what seemed to be volcanic rock, there turned out to be a layer of ice at least 200 feet thick. Cape Royds is actually an old glacier, descending from Erebus, that has been covered over by debris from the volcano. An airport built on such a surface would eventually melt what was underneath. It was during this survey that a tractor being driven over the ice by a U.S. seaman, R. T. Williams, broke through and the driver and tractor disappeared. Williams had been a popular young man and, as the first casualty of this expedition, the ice airfield near McMurdo was named in his honor.

In 1957 when the International Geophysical Year actually began, a party from New Zealand visited the huts at Royds and Evans. They felt that it was a matter of national pride, since these buildings lay in the Ross Dependency, that they be restored as shrines to honor the brave men who had lived in them. This was not easy, particularly at Evans, full of ice and, when this had been removed, still coated with black heavy grease from the seal blubber the men had used for heating. It took several year's work before Evans could be cleaned out but, in the process, a great number of objects were found buried in the ice that recalled the last occupation. As a result, while the hut at Royds is clean but spare, Evans still has a patina of grease but is full of things like canned foods, bottled preserves, laboratory equipment, notebooks, magazines, old clothes, bunks, and furniture that have been carefully put back into the places they seemed to belong as determined by old photographs. Visiting Cape Evans now, on a bright sunny day, when everything had all been tidied up, I did not find within myself a great sense of awe about the shrines I could actually see with my eyes. As visitors, we were too far away in time, too safe. (I have the same reaction at famous battlefields, great castles, and historic homes.) The geographical settings, of course, are quite spectacular as the explorers reported. What response *ought* I to have, I wondered as I walked around outside the building waiting for colleagues to finish their picture-taking. Alternately, I looked up at that glorious volcano and then down at the ground which I now observed was full of broken bones. I picked up one white piece, thinking it must be either from a seal or a pony, killed so that the men could survive. The helicopter was nearby. It sounded anxious to take off. Then I felt a kind of love for these badly equipped, ill-informed, unlucky, foolhardy, romantic, frozen, hungry, dirty, bearded men of a time so recent and so long ago, men so full of guts it was hard to believe they really existed. But here they were, the places where they had existed, and I had seen enough of the snow and the ice, the mountains and the crevasses, to have some idea of just how hard it was. Three hours to fly to the Pole, indeed! Well, wasn't that actually a better way to get there? In any case, you crazy men, I salute you. Just then, one of the pilots interrupted my thoughts. "You'd better put that bone down, sir. If any of the Kiwis catch you taking anything away from here, they'll cut your throat!"

CHAPTER VI

THE BASE OF THE KIWIS

THE Kiwis,* or New Zealanders, we met in the
Antarctic did not seem to be at all the sort of bloodthirsty
fellows suggested by the helicopter pilot. Scott Base, their
major installation on the continent, lies just two miles over
the hill from McMurdo Station. It is an easy drive and,
once past the hill that obscures the volcano from Mc-
Murdo, there is a great, unobstructed view of Mount
Erebus, serene, smoking, snow-covered white but with
many shades of blue and green, sunlit, very beautiful but
a potential menace to bother the Kiwi and Yankee installations. Wherever the snow is uncovered in this area
volcanic rubble is revealed, debris that has obviously come
from some eruption of Erebus—an event that clearly did
not occur very far in the past. Like people everywhere in
the world who live near obviously active volcanoes, the
residents do not seem to give a thought to its potential
danger. (Erebus was once thought to be the only active
volcano in the Antarctic. Others are now known to be
alive also, and Deception Island, off the Palmer Peninsula,

* Their nickname comes from the country's attractive little flightless
bird that exists no place else in the world.

100

recently became active enough to make resident scientists from three countries flee for their lives.)

Relations between men at the two bases seem excellent and much socializing goes on back and forth, even in the dead of winter. The existence of "someplace to go" makes life a little more bearable. McMurdo, being done in the lavish American way, is much larger and has a barber shop, a church, a hospital, a choice of movies, and three different clubs. Scott has huskies, seals, a club of its own, and an outgoing hospitality that, though offered with a kind of British accent, seems more in the style of the American West. Until very recently, of course, New Zealand was a frontier, and its main industry is ranching. The Kiwi attitude about strangers seems to be that a man is okay until he proves otherwise. In any case, we were greeted very warmly by the public information officer, a newspaperman taking time off from civilization for a summer season on the ice.

He first escorted us down a hill of ice and lava rubble and onto McMurdo Sound itself. Here, at the shore, are the beautiful milky-blue formations of pressure ice, crumpled where the frozen sea meets the land. But there are some level spots as well. On one of these levels, a man in our party was astonished to find the ice underneath him caving in. He had stepped on a crevice. He went down only to his calf and quickly recovered. Our guide, well used to the signs of crevices, pointed out that any thin white line might be deceptive and give way. A crevice might not be deep here by the shore, but a dunking in the water close to freezing temperature might be unpleasant. We walked with our eyes on the ground, pausing to look at the spectacular ice shapes, but not trying to see these and move at the same time. Some of the crevices were wide open and we had to make small jumps across them. Climbing some of the small ridges in rubber boots was slippery work and the best way down the other side seemed to be simply tobogganing on the seat of your pants. Then around a bend we saw a nursery of the Weddell seals.

There were perhaps a dozen big, fat mothers, each with her newborn pup. At about 800 pounds, they were too clumsy to move away from the intruders and much too maternal to leave their offspring. Actually, we did not seem to alarm them unless we came very close. Then the baby would huddle against the mother and she would give an indignant squawk, a sound hard to describe but clearly indicating an opinion that we had come too close. Since Weddells have no natural enemies on land, they have no true fear reaction. Slaughtering seals for food or fur must have been disgustingly easy. The adult females look grossly overweight, though this is their only protection against the cold. The pups, however, are immensely appealing, their large eyes betraying their complete innocence. Their appearance ought to bring out the paternal instinct of the toughest man. Fur seals, however, very similar in their appeal, were murdered by the millions in the last century for their pelts. They are now almost extinct. Fortunately for the Weddell seals, their fur, though useful to them, does not make good coats.

This birthing area near Scott Base is used by Weddells every austral spring. The crush of the pressure ice creates many holes by which they can easily re-enter the sea. In some ways the nursery is not too attractive, there being considerable excrement and blood from the afterbirth around, but this is certainly natural. The visitor is not at a nicely scrubbed zoo here. This is the Antarctic, and this is the way animals are born and cared for.

It was very quiet out on the ice. My companions were all going about their business, taking photographs of a spot that would be hard to forget with or without film. Being no cameraman, I simply looked about me. High above us was the great volcano. Beneath us the frozen sea. Nearby, the sculptures made by the ice. Across the Sound, the rosy tinted Society Mountains. All around us the miracle of birth in incredible conditions. Somewhat humbled, I walked back and up the hill to the man-made buildings of Scott Base.

Constructed as New Zealand's contribution to the International Geophysical Year, the base was to serve the nation's scientists and be headquarters for Sir Edmund Hillary's activities in support of Sir Vivian Fuchs' Commonwealth Trans-Antarctic Expedition. Hillary, the first man to climb Mount Everest, moved out from here with vehicles to set up a chain of supply dumps all the way to the South Pole. Sir Vivian would use these supplies on the last leg of his expedition, the first land crossing of the Antarctic continent. This project was successfully completed, but the Kiwis decided to stay on to continue studies, many of which needed the continuity of years to be of greatest value.

The base is somewhat dependent on U.S. support, at least for air transport. The New Zealanders use the Williams Field facility, in return for which New Zealand provides an air base for the U.S. Navy in Christchurch. The cooperation extends far beyond this, a pleasant example of what is possible between sovereign states. McMurdo supplies the weather forecast for both stations. Since they are only two miles apart, it would be ridiculous to duplicate this meteorological effort. New Zealand tankers have often brought in fuel to be stored at McMurdo. Instruments and information are often exchanged and, in addition, it is nice to have a friendly neighbor.

Although the scientific work at Scott and at several outlying bases may seem to parallel U.S. activities (the research is mostly in those areas of physics for which the Antarctic is uniquely suited), independent attacks on the same problem, from different points of view, have often had considerable value. There is usually more than one way of looking at a thing, as any two witnesses to the same event can testify. In addition to the work at Scott, the New Zealand Navy ship *Endeavour* conducts oceanographic research in the Antarctic seas and New Zealand itself serves as a base for various geophysical observations being made on a simultaneous, world-wide scale. Scott also serves as a training ground for graduate students in science. Not unimportantly, New Zealand maintains the base to make good on the claim, inherited from Great Britain, for a sizable portion of Antarctic land called the Ross Dependency. (Like all claims to Antarctic territory, the New Zealand claim is not recognized by the United States, but there are no hard feelings about it.)

Whether the United States recognizes the Ross Dependency or not, the postage stamps issued in its name create a brisk tourist business. Our first stop on a tour of the buildings, all under one roof to avoid going out in the cold, was to the post office. There the special stamps were on sale as well as a postcard, a picture of a dog team silhouetted against a glacier, that is the handsomest, if not the most representative, I have seen of the continent. New Zealand is thinking seriously of setting up tours for the more intrepid kind of traveler. Visitors would fly into

Williams, stay aboard a ship stationed there since there is no room at all at McMurdo or Scott, and make small journeys about Ross Island. There are numerous difficulties facing such a project but, and New Zealanders are quite resourceful, if they can be overcome, there will undoubtedly be customers.

At the time of our visit to Scott it was full of men to overflowing. Owing to the communications blackout, field parties had not yet spread out to begin the biology, geology, and mapping programs, but then suddenly planes began to fly again and more scientists poured in. Some had to sleep in their field tents outdoors, while others slept on cots in the post office. The men who winter over each have a room to themselves. The major Kiwi field party of the 1969–70 season explored the Robert Scott Glacier, unvisited since the Byrd expedition of 1933–35. The party was flown to the head of the glacier on the Polar Plateau by a U.S. Hercules. After their arrival they traveled by motor toboggans. At first they studied Mount Weaver, only 200 miles from the Pole, nearly the most southerly of exposed mountains. Mount Weaver has coal seams and fossils of leaves and stems. Lichens grow on the mountain at an altitude of 5000 feet. Then the party descended the ninety-mile glacier making studies of forms of life at various altitudes as well as doing research on the rocks. At the end of the trip they were picked up once more by the Hercules.

After a tour of the base, we were shown the vehicle used by Fuchs to cross the continent, and then we walked down a path about a quarter of a mile to see the dogs. We could hear them before we could see them. To hear barking seemed rather strange, and then I realized it was because, away from habitations, the Antarctic is usually so silent.

The animals, about twenty of them, were chained to stakes set around in a circle. Each dog had a decent amount of room around him but, to prevent any fights, no dog could quite reach another.

They were all big, healthy looking creatures, their glossy fur tan and black. The arrival of people excited them and they jumped up and down, wagging their tails. We were all a bit leery about approaching, but our guide said they were friendly, and they turned out to be exuberantly so. Some had Greenland names such as Uglen, Akortok, Kakiwa, Ardluk. Their diet was seal meat, and the New Zealanders had a special permit from the signers of the international Antarctic treaty to kill seals to feed them. The usual dog team was nine in number and they were exercised ahead of a sled almost every day, even during the long winter night. This pack of dogs is one of the last in the Antarctic. Officially, they are kept in case of an emergency when every vehicle may have broken down. In practice, they seem more or less for show and as companions for the isolated men.

As an example of the curious problems of support in the Antarctic, Admiral Welch had mentioned these huskie dogs at New Zealand's Scott Base. The Kiwis wanted to move some of their huskies from Hallett Base, some hundreds of miles away, to Scott Base. These dogs, imported from Greenland, never again leave the Antarctic continent. The pack at Scott Base had not been replenished from any outside source for several generations and there had been considerable inbreeding. Hallett was giving up its dog team and the infusion of fresh genes would be a great boon to the pack at Scott. Would the Navy fly the dogs over? The Admiral agreed, but said that the dogs would have to be crated. He would take no chances on how this semi-wild breed would behave aboard an aircraft. The Kiwis immediately agreed to crate them, but a problem arose. There was no wood in the Antarctic with which to build crates. They had to be brought in at a cost of $800 per crate.

A husky's working life is about eight years long, and after that they are painlessly put to death. When dog lovers in New Zealand discovered this, they stirred up a national crisis. If the dogs were no longer useful, it was asked, why not bring them back to New Zealand to live out their lives in retirement until they died a natural death? Many people offered to take care of them. The Government, however, mindful of the depredations caused by deer and other foreign animals after they had been introduced to a land that had never known them, refused to allow the huskies to be brought back from the Antarctic. They might break loose, run wild, and attack sheep. After all, they are part wolf.

No matter how they treat them eventually, the Kiwis at Scott Base are quite sentimental about their dogs. One Christmas not long ago they arranged that a Christmas tree be flown in as a treat for the animals. The dogs simply barked at the strange object and refused to use the tree as dogs have used trees since time immemorial. Born and raised in the Antarctic, they had never seen a growing thing and all the tree did was frighten them.

CHAPTER VII

A FEAST IN THE SOUTHERN OCEAN

Until the first airplanes landed at McMurdo Station in 1955 after a non-stop flight from New Zealand, no one had ever reached the Antarctic without traveling the sea that surrounds it. Captain Nat Palmer, the American who may have been the first person ever to sight the mainland, reached it aboard his little sealing ship, the *Hero*. Palmer probably first saw the land, about fifty miles away, from one of the high slopes of Deception Island, an elevation he had climbed while searching for eggs. Deception, one of the South Shetland chain due south of Argentina, was much favored by seagoing hunters of whales and seals because it has a virtually land-locked harbor about ten miles in diameter where ships can find safety during the wild storms that occur so frequently in this ocean. The harbor is probably a caldera, the interior of a volcano that has either subsided or blown itself to bits in an explosion of massive proportions. (Crater Lake in Oregon is another such caldera.) The elevations surrounding the harbor of Deception Island are the rim of the volcano. The harbor has only one entrance from the sea, partially concealed, the situation that gives the island its name. In Palmer's time, during the 1820s, the anchorage was known as Yankee Harbor. In recent years when so much research has been going on in the Antarctic, the waters around Deception Island have been taken over by teams of scientists from Chile, Argentina, and Great Britain. The bases they established there were considered to be safe havens. In December 1967, however, Deception's dormant volcano suddenly became very active and there were numerous earthquakes and eruptions that forced the evacuation of the fifty-two scientists then in residence. A Chilean plane flying over the scene a few days after the men had been rescued found the island completely obscured in a great mushroom cloud of smoke. The eruption has now subsided and research teams are cautiously coming back to see what changes were brought about by the event and, as in the case of the new volcanic island of Surtsey off Iceland, to see what forms of life have returned to establish their first footholds.

When James Clark Ross sailed into the Antarctic's perilous seas about twenty years after Palmer, his principal objective was to find the South Magnetic Pole. (Of course he failed because his ships, the *Erebus* and *Terror,* sailed into the Ross Sea instead, and he could not navigate to the magnetic pole because it was on the opposite side of the mountainous Victoria Land that bordered the sea he had inadvertently discovered.) The early explorers were not specialists and found interest in everything they encountered, including the biology of the sea. At one point Ross wrote in his log, "When the ships were in the high latitude of 77° 11′ south, a fish was thrown up by the spray in a gale of wind, against the bows of the *Terror.* It was carefully removed, and a rough sketch of it was made by the surgeon; but before it could be put into spirits, a cat carried it away from his cabin, and ate it."

The first formal study of the Antarctic water as such, the introduction of the science known as oceanography, began during the world-wide voyage of the *Challenger,* a converted ship of the Royal British Navy, between the years 1872 and 1876. The men on the *Challenger* took samples of sediments on the ocean floor during eleven stops for experiments (called stations) below the latitude of 50° South. The sediments nearest the continent were composed mainly of material from the land, much of it probably rafted north as the base of icebergs which sank when the iceberg melted. North of this was a broad area of diatom ooze, the remains of microscopic plants that thrive in arctic water. Still farther north the dominant sediments were globigerina ooze, the ubiquitous remnants of tiny, primitive ocean animals that can be found over much of the world's sea bottom. Before the IGY began, somewhat uncoordinated oceanographic work in the Antarctic was done in the Ross Sea during Byrd's second expedition (1933), by the Norwegian research vessel *Brategg* which made a six-month study of water composition and plant life in 1947, by the British research vessel *Discoverer II* which sailed all around the continent in 1950, and during the U.S. Operation High Jump of 1950 when a series of long sediment cores were taken in the Ross Sea. During this time the currents of the Antarctic seas were also being studied, but mostly by theory based on their apparent effects on water farther to the north. The most prominent feature of this part of the ocean, the Antarctic Convergence, one of the most fundamental boundaries in the world, had probably been known to predators such as whales, seals, and birds for millions of years because of the phenomenal feast it produces.

The water surrounding the Antarctic has been given a number of names. The Atlantic, the Pacific, and the Indian Oceans may all be considered to extend down to the continent itself, as they seem to do on a map, but the character of the sea has changed radically far north of the land itself. An invisible barrier exists that is so solid that fish to the north seldom venture to cross it and fish from the south retreat when the front has been reached. The various currents that isolate the Antarctic do not have exactly the same boundaries, but for practical purposes many oceanographers accept the parallel of 52° South. The water below this they call the Southern Ocean.

A general outline of the shores of the Southern Ocean had been drawn by explorers long before the IGY began. The map of the Antarctic is unfamiliar to many people. Antarctic geography has not been stressed in schools. To get one's bearings in a discussion of its seas, it is a good idea to relate it to some well-known feature, such as the narrow tip of South America. Directly below this is the long tentacle known to the Americans as the Palmer Peninsula. (To the British it is Graham Land. Neutrals call it the Antarctic Peninsula.) In addition to the British, Chilean, and Argentinian posts here, the United States maintains its Palmer Station, a base for scientific field parties and a port of call for oceanographic ships. To the west, or left, is the Bellingshausen Sea, named after the exploring Russian admiral. A Belgian party led by Adrien de Gerlache found their ship held fast by the Bellingshausen ice in 1898 and thus, without planning it, de Gerlache's group became the first to winter over in the Antarctic. Next to the west comes the Amundsen Sea, where Captain Cook made his deepest southern penetration. Then, after a long stretch of uncompromising coast, comes the Ross Sea and the Ross Ice Shelf. For much of the year, the Ross Sea is covered by ice pack, but Ross found open water to the Ice Shelf in January 1841, and Admiral Byrd was able to penetrate it to establish his various Little Americas on the edge of the shelf. McMurdo Sound, of course, lies at the western edge of the Ross Sea. From here the shore of Victoria Land stretches more or less due north toward New Zealand. At intervals the United States and New Zealand share the facilities of the small Hallett Station, near Cape Adare, the northern tip of Victoria Land.

After the enormous indentation of the Ross Sea, the coast of East Antarctica makes a neat arc past the Gates Coast, explored extensively by Australia's Douglas Mawson and on to the Adélie coast, named by its French discoverer, Dumont d'Urville, after his wife. The coast, the windiest place in the world, is presently the site of a French base. (A species of penguins, too, got its name from d'Urville's wife.) Quite some distance up this windy coast there is Wilkes Station, signed over to Australia by the United States, and then, at another considerable distance, the Russian base at Mirny. Then, farther on, the Australian stations named Davis and Mawson, and south of South Africa, two smaller Russian bases, with the Japanese Showa station between them, and the South African, Tottenbutka (or Sanae). The British Halley Bay station is next along the coast. The vast Weddell Sea completes the Antarctic circle back to the Palmer Peninsula. Almost as large as the Ross Sea, the Weddell is bordered in part by the Filchner Ice Shelf, a vast counterpart of the Ross Ice Shelf and one whose dimensions seem to increase every time it is surveyed. The Filchner Ice Shelf, like the Ross, frequently deposits huge icebergs in the sea.

Most of this enormous length of Antarctic coast has practically no continental shelf at all. Where it does exist it is nowhere near the depth usually considered an average around the world, about 600 feet, but more often at depths such as 1200 to 1800 feet. The Weddell and the Ross seas, and their accompanying ice shelves, have the only significant continental shelves, and at the edge of the Ross Sea shelf, before the plunge into the deep sea, the depth is about 2400 feet. In general, where Antarctic shelves do exist, the slope descends quite rapidly to depths of about 10,000 feet. There are three large basins within the Southern Sea and north of the continental slopes. One extends east from Scott Island, nead the end of the Ross Sea, east to the southern end of Chile. Its maximum depth was reported as about 19,000 feet. Another deep basin runs west from the Balleny Islands, a bit west of Cape Adare to the Kerguelen Islands Ridge in the Indian Ocean. Its greatest depth is around 17,000 feet. West of the Kerguelen Ridge, the East Pacific Rise, and so on. A remarkable feature of the Southern Ocean is its unusually deep continental shelves. One suggestion offered to explain these shelves is that the great load of ice on the land has caused the whole continent to sink as a unit.

The circulation of water in the Southern Ocean is brought about by the same causes that create currents elsewhere; by differences in temperature, by the rotation of the earth, by prevailing winds, and by the contour of the bottom. One of the most unusual phenomena of the Southern Ocean, the Antarctic Convergence, has already been mentioned. The Convergence circles the entire continent and the nearby islands between 60° and 48° South latitude. Here the cold waters of the Antarctic Seas, being more dense and heavier than the warm waters moving south from the tropics, plunge downward beneath it. The colder water is better able to hold quantities of dissolved oxygen and carbon dioxide. Its water is full of nutrient salts. The convergence of the cold and warm waters creates a rich soup in which plants and animals can thrive exuberantly. The Convergence is just about sixty miles wide, in a north-south direction. The Convergence is usually about 15° farther north in the East Atlantic than it is in the East Pacific, presumably because of the great amount of cold water that flows out of the Weddell Sea. Aboard a ship the entrance to the Antarctic Convergence is quite apparent. There is a considerable drop in temperature and an obvious increase in bird and fish life.

The Southern Ocean also has a vast east-flowing stream called the Antarctic Circumpolar Current. It is driven primarily by the winds that flow almost constantly from the west. This current carries water from its whole depth, from the surface to the bottom, and the quantities transported, although they have been estimated, seem almost impossible to imagine. (What does 120 million cubic meters per second mean?) The maximum flow of water occurs when the current meets the Antarctic Convergence in the East Atlantic.

Another interesting phenomenon of the Southern Ocean is the Antarctic Bottom Water. This usually originates in the Weddell Sea where local circumstances lead to the formation of very cold, salty water that sinks at the continental margin and flows north and east at temperatures about one-half a degree above freezing. The Antarctic Bottom Water is so heavy that it stays at levels below 12,000 feet and it can be found and identified far north of the Equator in the Atlantic. It is not as recognizable in the Pacific.

The Weddell Sea, source of the Antarctic Bottom Water, has also been a source of trouble to a number of explorers and scientists. The man who gave it his name was James Weddell, a Scottish sealer, who sailed his 160-ton ship, *Jane*, down to 74° 15′ South on February 20, 1823. This broke Captain Cook's record for latitude. Weddell was one of the few men who ever found this sea free from ice but, although the way was clear to continue south, he wisely decided to go no further because winter was very near.

Weddell was supposedly in the area to hunt, and he carried no scientific equipment, but he had great curiosity and brought four of the best chronometers obtainable to aid in navigation. His calculations of longitude were exceedingly accurate. Every day he made notations in his log of the air and water temperature and of magnetic variations on his compass. He captured several leopard seals, a breed of animal that delighted the scientists back in London. Before turning back from his record penetration to the south, Weddell issued a double ration of rum to his crew and threw a lead on a line over the side to measure the depth. It was 1476 feet.

Few ships ventured into the Weddell Sea until Wilhelm Filchner sailed down the western side of it in the season of 1911–12 aboard the ship *Deutschland* and found the ice shelf he named after himself. Then Ernest Shackleton entered the Weddell Sea in 1914, planning to land at its southern end and make a traverse across the whole continent to McMurdo Sound. His ship became completely beset in the ice on January 18, 1915. The story of how he and his men survived the ordeal that followed is one of the epic adventures of exploring. The cause of his trouble, the Weddell pack ice, has not changed with the passage of time. Weddell's clear sailing conditions have never been found since by later challengers. A prevailing southeast wind from the continent makes the ice pack circulate in a clockwise manner. The ice piles up against the shore of the Palmer Peninsula, then slowly works its way north in the current but then is prevented from breaking out into the open sea by the South Georgia Islands. While the western side of the Ross Sea is free of ice almost every summer, this practically never happens on the west side of the Weddell. In spite of the hitherto impenetrable ice cover this sea almost always presents, an international expedition was mounted in 1968 to force it to reveal its physical and biological properties. The sea's very recalcitrance seemed to spur researchers.

At first the plans were for ski-equipped airplanes or helicopters flying off icebreakers to carry field teams to desired points on the sea ice where the men would drill holes and lower sampling equipment. The operational difficulties of this approach were soon discovered and so the idea of an international survey was developed. This plan would use two icebreakers, ships that would carry scientists representing a number of different research interests. The United States assigned its most powerful icebreaker, the Coast Guard's *Glacier,* and Argentina offered its icebreaker, the *General San Martin.* The *Glacier* was modified to accommodate five laboratories, a satellite navigation system with equipment for recording satellite photos of the ice, plus many other kinds of special oceanographic equipment.

The basic idea of the big project was to place four instrumented buoys, developed by Norwegian scientists, on

Helicopter lands visitors near the historic hut of Sir Robert Falcon Scott at Cape Evans on Ross Island.

Hut built on Cape Evans by Captain Robert F. Scott and party in 1911.

The jawbone of a lystrosaurus (in the plastic cup, left) discovered in Antarctica December 4, 1969, has been called by American geologists "not only the most important fossil ever found in Antarctica but one of the truly great fossil finds of all times." The bones on the right were uncovered in the same area of the Queen Alexandra Range, 400 miles from the South Pole, but they have not yet been identified.

Coalsack Bluff (*center of photo*) in the Trans-Antarctic Mountains is scene of the historic fossil find. Geologists reached the area by helicopter.

Dr. E. H. Colbert and Dr. D. H. Elliot examine site of animal fossil discoveries in Trans-Antarctic Mountains.

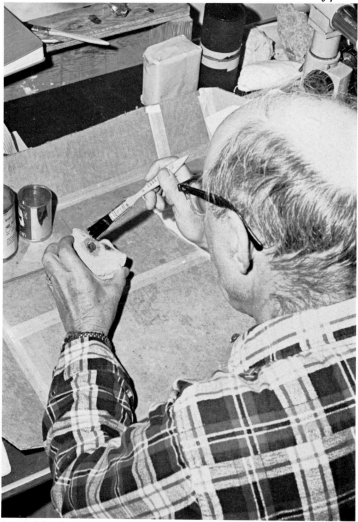

Dr. E. H. Colbert, a vertebrate paleontologist from the American Museum of Natural History, New York, and the Museum of Northern Arizona, Flagstaff, Arizona, studies fossil bones found in a sandstone bed at Coalsack Bluff, Trans-Antarctic Mountains.

Plastic bags are used to transport soil samples back to camp for later study.

Jon S. Powell, from the University of Arizona, Tucson, chips bone out of sandstone at Coalsack Bluff, Trans-Antarctic Mountains.

Visitors arriving for lunch at the South Pole. Aircraft in background is a U.S. Navy Hercules.

William J. Breed chipping fossil bone out of sandstone at Coalsack Bluff.

The isolated USS *Burton Island* is shown in the background of the joint New Zealand–United States scientific station at Hallett. Adélie penguins are in foreground.

Weddell seal emerging through slush-filled hole in McMurdo Sound.

An Adélie penguin with her two baby chicks at Cape Crozier.

Weddell seal on the ice near McMurdo Station.

A Weddell seal and her pup laze under the Antarctic sun at Hutton Cliffs about 13 miles from McMurdo Station.

Bone of labyrinthodont, the first animal fossil discovered in the Antarctic. Found by Dr. Peter J. Barrett in 1967.

Sandstone Bluff, at the top of which the labyrinthodont bone was found. Dave Johnston marks the spot on the West Ridge of Graphite Park.

ANTARCTICDEVRON SIX helicopter over Taylor Valley with the Hughes Glacier in the background.

Dr. D. H. Elliot geologizing to learn the continent's past in the Trans-Antarctic Mountains.

The Coast Guard icebreaker USS *Burton Island* docks at McMurdo
Station during the summer season when the Ross Sea is navigable.

(*Left to right*) USS *Burton Island,* USS *Atka,* and the USS *Glacier*
push together to move huge iceberg from channel of broken ice
leading to McMurdo Station.

The first women ever to visit the South Pole. November, 1969.

Kay Lindsay, Terry Tickhill, and Lois Jones of the Ohio State scientific team finish packing and get ready to board the helicopter that will take them back to McMurdo Station.

Sun and clouds hang dramatically over Crater Hill high above McMurdo Station.

the continental slope of the Weddell Sea where they would measure temperatures and current speeds and directions at one-hour intervals. One of the buoys also carried a multiple water sampler provided by Professor H. Stommel of M.I.T. The information derived from these instruments would be recorded on magnetic tapes with enough storage capacity to record fourteen months of observations. The buoys were to be placed at a depth of about 2100 feet, but about sixty feet from the bottom. Each buoy had an acoustic release mechanism so that it could release its anchor weight on signal and rise to the surface for recovery. The purpose of the measurements was to determine how and why the unusual Antarctic Bottom Water develops in the Weddell Sea. The four buoys were to be placed in about the same latitude that James Weddell had once found to be ice-free. They would remain in position for one year and be retrieved at the end of this time. Beyond placing the buoys and getting them back, fifty-three oceanographic stations were planned for the *Glacier* during the two-year program, stations at which water measurements would be made and the geology and biology of this unknown region studied.

Early satellite photos suggested that ice conditions in the Weddell Sea would be relatively light during the first season, and the *Glacier* and *San Martin* sailed with high hopes. (The *Glacier* first had to wait for six days in Punta Arenas, Chile, for the arrival of the water sampler from M.I.T.) The *Glacier* took water samples in the Drake Passage between South America and the Palmer Peninsula and in the Scotia Sea far down in the South Atlantic. Two rendezvous were made with the *San Martin,* one at the Argentina Station Esperanza on the Peninsula and one out at sea about 70° South, to exchange scientific information. En route to the buoy laying, the *Glacier* tagged four enormous icebergs for possible charting of their later movements. The buoys were placed in the planned positions and the *Glacier* proceeded on to its scheduled stations. This program was interrupted when the *Glacier* had to steam hundreds of miles out of its way to put a medical emergency ashore at the British Halley Bay Station. Then considerable revisions of the planned stations had to be made because of worsening ice conditions and lengthening periods of darkness as the ship sailed north. The time schedule for stops at stations was shortened but operations by scuba divers and by animal census parties, placed on ice floes by boat or helicopter, were carried out.

Altogether, the *Glacier* and *San Martin* occupied seventy stations, more than twice the number planned for the first season. Sufficient information was obtained to prepare a good bathymetric chart of the Weddell Sea bottom and new techniques were worked out for acquiring physical data even when the sea was completely covered with ice. About eighty percent of the *Glacier's* trip in the Weddell Sea was through ice, and ninety percent of the stations occupied were in areas where no oceanographic research had ever been done before.

In 1969 the *Glacier* and *San Martin* returned to the Weddell Sea. This time the *Glacier* could not get closer than fifty-five miles to the position of the submerged buoys. The following year the Coast Guard ship returned once more and managed to sail within twenty-two miles of its target but could proceed no further because of heavy ice concentration. A helicopter was sent over the position but found the ice too thick for any kind of buoy rescue work that might be improvised. In addition, the *Glacier's* hull had been damaged, so, for safety's sake, the expedition had to be called off.

The National Science Foundation has now abandoned efforts to retrieve the buoys. They will leave them "as artifacts to be discovered by men of some future age." However, if a satellite should one season show open ice at the location, and if a ship is available at the same time, another attempt may be made.

The astonishing tour of the Antarctic given to guests of the U.S. Government gives the impression that it is all so easy now. The flights to McMurdo, Byrd Station, and the Pole have indeed become quite dependable and life at McMurdo is certainly no hardship. These places are just footholds, however, and trouble can easily develop at any of them. When evaluating something like this attempt to crack the secrets of something as obdurate as the Weddell Sea, one is reminded that the frozen continent is still master of the situation. One of its ice-filled seas, with an area about the same as that of Alaska, will certainly continue to resist even the most ingenious and determined efforts of the scientists and sailors.

Still the recent forays into the Weddell Sea have yielded by-products. One of the most interesting observations made in this terrible water is the richness of life that it contains. A common-sense assumption easy to make is that hardly anything could survive such harsh conditions. The average water temperature down to 3000 feet is several degrees below freezing zero. What could live in water like this or on a surface covered with thick ice most of the time? Surveys taken from the *Glacier* showed that large numbers of many groups of large fishes lived in the top 3000-foot layer of water. A thick bloom of phytoplankton covering about 6000 square miles of sea surface was found near the Filchner Ice Shelf in February 1968. In March 1969, an even greater bloom stretching over some 20,000 miles of water was found about 150 miles north of the buoy positions. The scientists interested in making an animal population census found large numbers of crabeater seals and Adélie penguins on the ice and snow petrels flying overhead. Other kinds of seals and emperor penguins were also sighted but were less numerous. The waters of the Weddell Sea, like all those surrounding the Antarctic, are amazingly productive. They are a priceless laboratory for marine biologists.

It is hardly surprising that whales were the first animals of the Southern Ocean to be studied seriously by scientists. They not only represented a source of wealth, they were also intrinsically so interesting. To find out about whales, their migration routes, their distribution, their breeding behavior, and their food habits all came under scrutiny. In turn, this led to some general conclusions about the Southern Ocean. It was concluded that it was remarkably uniform, that the sea's physical characteristics varied little around the entire continent. It was also found that, in comparison to other seas, this sea contains very few different species but those that it did have, it had in countless numbers. (The reverse is the case in tropical waters.)

Curiosity about the diet of whales led to a consideration of the food chain in the Southern Ocean. As is true everywhere, the base of the ladder is phytoplankton, the microscopic floating plants. It was found that the Southern Ocean contained nitrates and phosphates, the salts these plankton need for existence, in an abundance not matched in any other ocean. It was learned that blue and fin whales, two of the most valuable species commercially, subsist on shrimp-like creatures called "krill" or *Euphausia superba*. The supply of krill depends on the supply of phytoplankton. Thus it was discovered that the number of whales that an area could support could be estimated by measuring the nitrate and phosphate content of the water.

Later investigations concerned squid. They probably live on krill and other crustaceans, but this is hard to prove because they are about the most difficult marine animals to capture. They must be very numerous in the Southern Ocean, however, because the remains of their beaks are frequently found in the stomachs of whales, sea birds, and seals. The 100,000 elephant seals, for instance, that frequent the islands of South Georgia, live solely on squid. (Emperor penguins and crabeater seals feed almost entirely on species of krill.) In the course of these studies it was learned that the dominant phytoplankton of Antarctic waters were diatoms, tiny single-celled plants not usually visible to the naked eye except when they flourish in great numbers and stain the sea water brown.

Studies of the ocean bottom with dredges and more particularly by bottom photography show that it is quite heavily populated. Sponges and mollusks thrive in this cold region. Researchers have found that few species of mollusk are presently in evidence, but that many new families of mollusks are invading Antarctic waters on a major migration route that runs from South America through the islands of the Scotia Arc. Many parts of the ocean bottom have been found to be coated with a thick layer of living, rooted, branching colonial animals. The main food for bottom (benthic) animals is the supply of plankton remains that filters down, particularly during the summer. The various kinds of fixed organisms build right on top of one another since there is an advantage to the species that can reach above its fellows. In general it is believed that animal life in the Antarctic consists of a few ancient groups that have survived the onset of glacial conditions and do not closely resemble species in other areas, a larger group related to fauna in nearby deep waters, and a new group now moving in from the north.

During the IGY, oceanography in Antarctic waters did not receive much attention. Ships such as the Russian *Ob* and *Lena* made some observations, mostly in the sea around their base at Mirny, but their major work was as support vessels and, for research, their major contribution was to launch aircraft that flew on mapping expeditions over the land. The U.S. icebreaker *Glacier* and the New Zealand frigate *Pukaki* made new measurements of the Antarctic Convergence temperature, but such activities were only incidental to their primary assignments.

Highly organized science in the Southern Ocean began with the appearance of the National Science Foundation's research ship *Eltanin,* which began its astonishing series of cruises in 1962.

The *Eltanin* was built originally as a supply ship for radar stations in the Arctic. Its bows are designed to slip over the ice rather than crush it. Since the *Eltanin* was intended for work in the Arctic, it had been named after a star in the far northern constellation Draco. Though the name remains, when it was decided to assign the ship to the NSF for Antarctic work, its cargo holds were refitted with four new laboratories, staterooms for scientists, and large anti-roll tanks to keep the ship reasonably stable in the rough southern waters. Weighing just less than 4000 tons, the ship carries a crew of forty-eight men and has accommodations for thirty-eight male or female scientists.

A trip aboard the *Eltanin* is not a pleasure cruise. Sailing either from Chile, New Zealand, or Australia, each voyage lasts about sixty days. Land is hardly ever seen—only cold gray skies, whitecaps, and ice. The ship serves all marine science. On one early voyage the work included studies of the basic biology in the Convergence, as well as observations of plankton, gravity, magnetism, airborne insects, radio signals from California, and investigation of geological links between South America and the Antarctic, ocean currents from the bottom of the sea to the surface, and a comparison of southern auroras with those of the north. Such a variety of projects may seem confusing, but the program is based on two very practical necessities.

Oceanographic work is not instant science. The results come not from wonderful moments when great truths are revealed but from tremendous masses of observations taken at many places on every possible occasion. Accumulation of data takes time, and a ship like the *Eltanin* costs thousands of dollars every day it is in operation. The luxury of a single objective cannot be afforded.

The *Eltanin's* record for hard work produces a sense of awe. With five or six cruises every year, each taking about two months, it is at sea more than eighty percent of the time, in the world's worst oceans. Since 1962 it has gone to the shipyard only once for overhaul. As of this writing it has traveled more than 450,000 miles.

The U.S. taxpayers spend about $1.5 million every year for the operation of this ship. Do they get their money's worth? Compare a few reports selected at random with other, better publicized uses of the Federal revenue. A Russian guest, N. F. Kudriavtsev, wrote of his experience for a Soviet scientific journal. "The author participated as an exchange scientist aboard the *Eltanin* on the seventh and eighth voyages from Feb. 4 to June 19, 1963. The ship explored the oceanic areas of the Falkland, South Orkney, South Sandwich and South Shetland Islands, the Drake Passage and the South Sandwich Trench.

"The geophysical observations consisted of recording and measuring whistlers, cosmic noise, airglow, radio noise at eight frequencies, and the total components of the geomagnetic field.

"In the field of oceanology, a variety of observations of waves, water temperature, salinity and chemical composition were made.

"Standard meteorological observations of the lower atmosphere were conducted; in addition the program included radiosonde investigations of the upper atmosphere, measurements of ozone and carbon dioxide content, compilation of maps for weather analysis, and experimental studies of precipitation measurements.

"Studies were conducted on the zoo- and phytoplankton, photosynthetic plankton, bacteria at various depths and in bottom sediments, antibiotics in new microorganisms, vitamins in bottom sediments, bottom organisms and bathypelagic fauna. The ecology and adaptability of organisms in Antarctic waters were studied.

"The hydrogeologic investigations consisted of sediment sampling, photographing the ocean floor, and depth soundings along the entire track.

"Hydrochemical and entomological investigations were also conducted."

This is an almost complete catalog of what oceanography is all about. Apparently the Russian visitor was impressed.

On the fourteenth cruise in the summer of 1964, Clyde Roper caught 167 cephalopods (squid) representing fifteen species. He tried to keep them alive in a thirty-gallon aquarium with a refrigerator unit. He found a species with a buoyant mechanism by which it can hang suspended at the desired depth (about a mile down) without having to expend energy by continuous swimming. This cruise covered 8000 miles in two months.

Peter C. Harper of the Dominion Museum in Wellington, New Zealand, wrote about the *Eltanin*'s bird research program in 1965. His purpose was to study the seasonal distribution and relative abundance in the Antarctic and sub-Antarctic. About 1900 photographs of forty-five species of sea birds were obtained. Over 100 birds were collected, representing twenty species. A rookery of over 10 million chinstrap penguins were found on Zavodovski Island.

Researchers from the Lamont Geological Observatory in New York were aboard on six cruises of the *Eltanin* in 1965. The ship made 144 hydrographic stations (pauses for measurement taking). The Lamont men made 2465 bathythermograph observations on these cruises. (This instrument, called the BT, measures water temperature and density and is the most commonly used oceanographic tool.)

As of June 1, 1966, the *Eltanin* had collected 5,350,000 marine specimens. The greater part of these went to the Smithsonian Institution, which acts as the national repository for such material. So many cores had been taken for the marine geological program that Florida State University, where most of them will be preserved and studied, had to open a new building to house them. In 1966 the ship received its satellite navigation equipment (the new system that revolutionized finding a ship's position at sea), steamed 35,795 nautical miles, and began the paleomag-

Laboratory at the Bottom of the World

netic studies of sediment cores. The study of ancient magnetism in rocks has turned out to be one of the most solid
proofs of the continental drift theory.

In 1967 the *Eltanin* paid its first visit to McMurdo Station as part of its maiden cruise into the Ross Sea. The ship
spent 313 days of the year at sea and at various times
accommodated scientists from Australia, Chile, France,
New Zealand, and the United Kingdom, doing its part to
promote the greatest possible interchange among nations
in the Antarctic. During this year it had its one overhaul
in San Francisco but still managed to log 37,177 miles in
scientific cruises. The saga of the *Eltanin* continues,
though it is no longer the lone wolf of the Southern Ocean.

Early in 1969 she was joined by the National Science
Foundation's new ship, the research vessel *Hero*, length
125 feet, displacement 650 tons, with a complement of ten
crewmen and ten scientists. This smaller ship, the first
ever to be based in Antarctica, was named for Captain Nat
Palmer's original sloop, and the *Hero*, appropriately, will
operate for seven months of the year from the new Palmer
Station that the U.S. Navy has built on the peninsula to
support it.

The *Hero* has been built of wood to better withstand
severe ice conditions. The hull of white oak almost two
feet thick will bend without breaking under stress that
could make steel ships crack. To resist the sharp cutting
edges of the ice, the hull is sheathed with a tough hard-
wood called greenheart. The *Hero* has both Diesel engines
and sails. The sails permit it to maneuver in case of damage to the main propulsion plant but the main purpose
of the sails is to steady the ship and keep it quiet during
special research measurement. During the austral summer
the *Hero* will act as transport for all activities from Palmer

Station, placing field parties along the shores of the peninsula and on adjacent islands and carrying personnel and material to and from South America. In the southern fall and spring, the ship will be used for surveys of fish masses, seal herds, whale migrations, and bird populations. When conditions in the Southern Ocean become too severe the *Hero* will operate out of Punta Arenas, Chile.

The *Eltanin* has been concerned with all the sciences of the sea but the new, complementary team of the *Hero* and Palmer Station will be devoted largely to marine biology. The sea between the tip of the Palmer Peninsula and South America is, even for the Southern Ocean, unusually productive of life. The obvious, practical reason for this intensified study of biology is that food from the sea is looked upon as one of the hopes for feeding the world's exploding population.

Although the Southern Ocean is obviously full of marine animals, the rough population of only a few species is known. How many of any kind of fish can be caught before they, like this area's once flourishing blue whales, are brought to the point of extinction? Are any kinds of fish ignored, like the anchovies off Peru used to be, that might be very valuable to mankind? What are the migration patterns of the Antarctic fish? When and where can they best be captured? These are some of the "big think" questions, and the answers may be very useful. The scientists will pursue these matters, though not exclusively. They will also continue to classify and try to understand all the interesting kinds of marine life in the Antarctic that seem to do nothing for human beings except excite their curiosity. Among these are the penguins and the seals, at once so familiar and exotic. They are creatures of the sea but they must breed on land, or at least on ice.

How should they be classified? They are certainly not fish. The scientists seem willing to leave this problem alone. They have other questions about penguins and seals, the trademarks of the Antarctic, that fascinate them much more. Most of the U.S. studies of these animals are carried on at McMurdo Sound, where penguins are abundant and conveniently near.

CHAPTER VIII

PENGUINS, SEALS, AND
BLOODLESS FISH

From time to time startled men at McMurdo Station have seen an Adélie penguin wandering down the
street. No one has been able to explain why the birds
choose to visit, but they are, of course, harmless and usually permitted to go on their way unmolested. Presumably,
in time, they will swim back to Cape Royds, the nearest
Adélie rookery, but clearly these vagrant birds are not
nesting that season, because the production and care of
an infant penguin is a full-time occupation for both its
mother and father.

One of the most sought-after excursions from McMurdo
Station is the tour of the Adélie rookery at Royds. The
newspaper group of which I was a member went there in
two helicopters on a brilliantly sunny afternoon. A helicopter is a marvelously easy way to go sightseeing, and on
this brief trip of twenty miles we had a wonderfully clear
view of stately Mount Erebus, of the glaciers that flowed
down from it and ended in sheer ice cliffs at the edge of
the McMurdo ice pack itself, views of icebergs frozen into
the sea, of small islands often populated with little seal

colonies, and then of Cape Royds itself, the place where Shackleton built his hut near an Adélie nursery. We made a wide circle around the Cape itself. There are very strict regulations about flying over or near penguins ever since a curious airplane, taking photographs for a census of birds at a rookery, flew so low that the birds panicked and fled, leaving behind them a hideous mess of broken eggs. Penguins are said to be fearless but this is not entirely true. An American researcher somehow managed to take the temperature of an Adélie penguin at the moment it was being disturbed by a flying helicopter and found that the bird's temperature had risen two degrees above normal. Our craft landed about a half-mile away, and we walked over the ice and rubble to the site where thousands of them almost completely covered two small hills. Coming closer you could see that the nests were separated from each other by about a foot, the nest being a circle of stones in the middle of which an erect little bird, with a black head and back and a white breast, sat on its egg. Visually, it is impossible to distinguish between the males and the females. Each mate takes its turn brooding while the other returns to the sea, at the bottom of the hill, in order to eat. The birds saw us but did nothing unless one approached too closely, and then they would set up a squawk that most closely resembled the sound of an old Model T Ford engine. Most unbirdlike. Some of the penguins kept getting up from their nests to wander around. Their intention was larceny. They were out to steal stones from some other penguin's nest. In this, they were usually successful. They would pick up a little stone, actually a bit of lava, from someone else's circle and scoot home, actually quite swiftly, while the victim loudly complained.

Sooner or later, however, he too would make a foray and steal from someone else.

Researchers have discovered that, during courtship, these stones are extremely important. An anxious male seeks out a stone, suitably rounded, and presents it to a female he hopes will be agreeable. If she accepts it, the stone becomes part of the nest. (The base of the nest, of course, endures from one season to the next.) Rounded stones are not easy to find, and that is why penguins steal them. While scientists were trying to understand this thieving they tried painting them blue, white, yellow, and red, so the men could recognize them. All the colored stones moved rapidly around the colony but the red stones moved fastest. Males were most eager for the red stones and the females accepted them most readily. Yet birds' eyes can distinguish only between black and white. It is not clear why red stones became so popular.

While the Adélies' stones obviously have symbolic meaning they also serve a function as well. As the summer advances, and before the eggs are hatched, the snow sometimes melts under the sun and water begins to trickle down the hill. The little stone nests, not more than two or three inches high, suffice to keep the cold water, which would be fatally chilling, away from the egg. Adélies probably use stones for nests because they are the only loose material available in the barren environment.

Adélie penguins were first seen by the French expedition of Dumont d'Urville in 1860, but they did not become symbols of the Antarctic until Byrd set up his Little America bases at the edge of the Ross Ice Shelf. Adélies were fairly common in the sea and much photographed because they were so "cute," so striking, so human in the way they walked, and so appealing in their trust of humans. In spite of their appeal, however, they do not become pets. Scientists find them uncommonly interesting because they are so unlike any other bird in existence.

Adélies and emperor penguins are the birds familiar to most people, but thirteen other species also exist. The family name comes from two Welsh words meaning "white head," a name given originally to a North Atlantic bird, now extinct, that was also known as the Great Auk. Auks had only a very distant relationship to the birds now bearing their name.

Penguins exist only in the Southern Hemisphere. They belong to a very ancient, primitive family that specialized for life in the sea. Among birds that cannot fly, only penguins have the keeled breast-bone found in all flying birds, but they have no flight feathers. As embryos, however, they do have flight quills, so they must have evolved from ancestors who did fly in the very distant past. Penguin wings do not have a joint that bends. They are the only birds without elbows. Their wings have become stiff flippers and their flying is done only in the water. Penguin fossils show that they existed in their present range at least 50 million years ago, when modern birds were just beginning to evolve. These fossil penguins are not a great deal different from their descendants. The species probably lost its ability to fly about 100 million years ago. It is easy to see why flying would fall into disuse if conditions within their range were anything like they are today. The Antarctic continent itself and the lands around it are so barren and the seas are so full of food that the adaptation to a swimming existence seems almost inevitable. Penguins swim better under the sea surface than on it. When in a hurry, they stay completely submerged and only leap out of the water momentarily to get a breath of air. It is believed they can swim faster than twenty-five miles an hour. They have achieved this remarkable swimming ability at the expense of much ability to protect themselves on land. On land, however, the Adélies have only one predator to worry about, the skua bird, because the skuas break open and eat unguarded eggs and also kill penguin infants. The emperor penguins have settled the predator problem by nesting on ice in the dead of winter, but such weather also takes its toll.

Adélie penguins spend the entire winter at sea which, even if the water is at freezing temperature, is warmer than the land. In the sea they have two enemies, leopard seals and killer whales, which do take a toll, but obviously enough Adélies manage to elude the predators to keep the population in balance. No one is sure where the Adélies roam in winter but the ones who return to Cape Royds to mate in the October spring must first travel long distances from the open ocean over the Ross Sea which still is frozen. On ice they often flop on their bellies and toboggan along as fast as a man can run.

Young Adélies are not very successful breeders. They return later in the season to the rookery than older ones and so there is less time to mate and reproduce. Once a young male has proved himself as a parent at one site, however, he returns to it in the following seasons nearly 100 percent of the time. Females are less consistent, only about thirty percent of them returning to the same mate and site in subsequent years. It takes Adélies about six years to become "established" breeders.

Adélies usually lay either one or two eggs. The parents take turns sitting on the egg to keep it warm, the mate who has been relieved of duty returning to the sea to eat. They continue this pattern after the chicks are hatched,

one parent after the other bringing back food which is
regurgitated into the infant's mouth. Scientists have been
very interested in Adélie behavior after the chicks leave
their nests, twenty-one days following birth. For the next
five weeks they congregate with other chicks in large clus-
ters while their parents are away at sea. When a parent
returns it goes to its empty nest and begins to make
sounds. The one or two chicks belonging to the adult return immediately to the nest. Other chicks may also appear. The parent begins to make special sounds to which
his offspring reply in a way the parent can recognize. It
drives off chicks that do not belong. Then the parent runs
away, pursued by his child or children. This very active
phase is called the "feeding chase" because the infant is
fed mostly during pauses in the run. During the chase
the birds cover many hundreds of yards. If the chick is
lost during the chase, it and the parent return to the site
and the program is repeated again. This makes it certain
that the parent will feed no one but its own young. The
scientists are trying to understand the sounds by which
the identification is made. A typical rookery is full of
thousands of birds and, to a human, they all seem indis-
tinguishable. It might be remembered that a human being
cannot by sight tell the difference between a male and
female Adélie either.

Adélies have a remarkable ability to navigate. How they
do it is unknown, but it is clear that the sun is involved.
One Adélie was taken 180 miles from its rookery at Cape
Crozier and was followed as it returned, traveling in an
absolutely straight line. The only time it acted confused
was when the sun was clouded over. In other experiments
of the same kind, Adélies have returned to their own rookery after being released 2000 miles away. Another inter-

esting question about penguins is the location of their "biological clock"—the mechanism that tells them, when they are far out at sea, that it is time to return home to mate. Presumably the signal is the return of the sun after the long dark night, but what is triggered in the bird that makes it obey its instinct? And how do birds nesting at Cape Royds find it again and even the same nest after an absence of six months or more?

Adélie and emperor penguins capture all their food, fish, krill, and squid, in the sea. They do not know how to eat on land. When taken to zoos they have to be force-fed for weeks before they learn how to handle the fish thrown to them. These birds are unique in their ability to go without eating for long periods of time. Among Adélies the fast may be for as much as a week, but a male emperor penguin has to go without food for more than four months.

One of the largest emperor rookeries in the Antarctic is at Cape Crozier, on the far end of Ross Island from McMurdo Station. It was during his scientific mission to the emperors at Cape Crozier that young Cherry-Garrard went through "the worst journey in the world." Emperors are the largest of all penguins, about four feet tall. They are the only birds in the world that begin to breed in the fall rather than spring. This makes the investigations of scientists very difficult because the most interesting part of the emperor breeding cycle occurs in the months when temperatures are often 40 degrees below and winds may reach 100 miles an hour. As has been said, such conditions keep predators away.

Adult emperors come ashore on the ice as winter is beginning late in March. Proved breeders always choose the same spot on the ice near the coast they had used during the previous successful season. They build no nests. After the ceremonies of courtship have taken place (the males sing something resembling a love song), the female lays her egg in May, just as the sun is setting for the winter. The male almost immediately places it on his feet and covers it with the lower part of his body in a special pouch that has evolved which keeps the egg at almost the same body temperature as the parent's. The female returns to the sea, first having to cross, at this season, about 125 miles of ice shelf. She has not eaten for seven or eight weeks, since she came on the ice. The males huddle together during the long, bitter night, incubating the egg for between sixty-two and sixty-four days. If an egg is exposed even for a moment the embryo is killed. There is a high mortality since it must be difficult even for the patient male emperor to remain almost still in such weather for more than two months. During this period he loses between fifty and seventy-five pounds. Still, in August, when the chick hatches, he has saved enough food in his crop to feed it for one or two days. Then the female, exactly on schedule, appears on the ice, often using her belly as a toboggan, full of food, to relieve her mate. The starved male goes to the ocean for several weeks of feeding, always returning by late in August. For the next three months the parents take turns feeding the infant. By early December the young emperor is able to take care of itself in the open sea and the whole family departs. Driven by nature's terrible pressure to reproduce, the adults have only until March before they must return to the shore ice to begin the whole cycle again.

Present-day research on the purely Antarctic penguins concerns the emperor's remarkable ability to make deep dives, population studies of both emperors and Adélies, the Adélies' skill at navigation, and the alarming fact that the fatty tissues of both breeds now reveal the presence of DDT, a substance that has never been used in the Antarctic. Does it come from imported food that has to be disposed as garbage at the U.S. and New Zealand bases on Ross Island, from air or ocean currents, from a concentration in krill, or from animals out of waters to the north that the penguins have fed upon? The day has already arrived when the Antarctic has a pollution problem.

Two other penguins, parenthetically, are of some scientific interest. One is the Humboldt penguin who, through no fault of his own, solved the problem of how all marine birds get rid of the great amounts of salt they ingest, far too much salt to be handled by the kidneys. A Humboldt penguin was forced to take in five grams of sodium chloride. Within ten minutes after the salt was taken, a clear colorless liquid started to drip from the tip of his bill. It was found that the penguin has glands in its skull that extract the salt and convey it to the nasal cavity. To get rid of the salty drop the penguin simply shakes his head with a gesture that can be observed in all sea birds.

The other penguin is the rare macaroni penguin that lives only on Heard Island in the Southern Ocean. This penguin always lays two eggs, one quite large and the other considerably smaller. The bird sits on both of the eggs but only the larger one ever hatches. What possible evolutionary function can be performed by such behavior?

The first men ever to venture into McMurdo Sound found Adélies and emperors, and they also found breeding Weddell seals. Luckily for the seals their thin coats of hair were of no interest to the explorers, but seal meat could be eaten and the blubber burned for light and heat. The Weddells were numerous, moreover, and, after surviving the first invasions, men left them alone for almost forty years, and then the newcomers had more interesting food and better fuel. Weddells thus became nothing but curiosities to most visitors and of great interest only to scientists. At Scott Base we had looked at them in the manner of tourists, but then one evening at McMurdo we were invited to drive out on the ice to observe the seals through the eyes of scientists.

At the bottom of the hill where McMurdo Station meets the Sound we boarded a little bus for the ride to the seal house. It was evening, not dark, of course, but a strange sort of half-light. There was no road out on the McMurdo ice but our National Science Foundation friend made his way as best he could by following the red flags posted along the course. After a trip of eight or perhaps ten miles on the featureless plain, we stopped in front of a little shed. Beyond this structure we could see a number of great mounds of animal, Weddell mamas. This was the domain of Donald Siniff and his colleagues from the University of Minnesota. The leading scientist came out to greet us. He suggested showing us his seals in small groups of only two people. Weddells may not fear man, but they do get upset and, if their pups are molested too much, the mothers will simply abandon them. In addition, many of the seals had been wired with radios that reported on their normal physiology and he did not want the seals disturbed by visitors who might alter the animals' normal patterns by charging about. I went along with the first group. It was about nine in the evening, daylight of a sort but it was cloudy, the sun could not be seen, and it seemed to be twilight. As we approached one large female and her pup, skua birds who had been feeding on the afterbirth flew away in front of us.

There were more than thirty females lying on the ice but only thirteen pups. The rest would be born in the next few days, but some of the females would probably be barren. Even though infertile, however, such females would go through the instinctive spring ritual in which the breed migrates to the blow holes created by the pack ice near the shore, just before the ice begins to break up, and the males wait in the water while the ungainly females lift themselves out of the water and lie waiting in the life-giving air for their time of labor. The pups are born weighing about fifty-five pounds. They have no hair at birth. They gain five to seven pounds a day from the rich mother's milk, but she can give them no warmth, no cuddling against the temperatures that may be many degrees below zero. How do the hairless infants survive? It seems that they do not shed all the placenta until they are a week or more old, and this membrane along with a very fine fur is sufficient protection. The internal temperature of a Weddell seal is 100 degrees Fahrenheit, but at the surface of the skin it is only five degrees warmer than the surroundings. Thus, if it is 40 below a thermometer on a Weddell's skin will register 35 below.

A Weddell female will nurse an orphan pup but will not teach it to swim. The agile little babies who have the right mothers begin to learn swimming as soon as they get rid of the sack around them. At most blow holes, which the pups must use to enter their other natural medium, there is usually a male waiting and blocking the way. The determined mother drives him away and coaxes her little one into the water. The mother eats nothing while nursing her child and usually loses 200 or 300 pounds during this period.

Weddell seals are not considered monogamous, but no one knows certainly since they mate in the sea, where humans have difficulty in observing them. The females are fertile soon after the babies have been weaned and are able to find their own fish. The males waiting at the blow holes are there only to breed. This takes place very soon after weaning. After impregnation, however, the fertilized egg does not begin to grow immediately. There is a dormant period of almost three months. Then gestation begins and the cycle is timed with such refinement that the female is ready to give birth just as the Antarctic spring begins the following year. This is just before the ice sheet begins to break up so the female has a solid surface on which to perform her function and nurture her baby until it has developed enough to take care of itself in the sea to which its mammal ancestors made only a partial adaptation many millions of years ago. In the exquisite rhythm of this cycle, the sea is just beginning its season of maximum food productivity at the time when the fast-growing, hungry infant has its greatest need of nurture.

There was blood around the seals Siniff showed us that was not due to afterbirth. The blood had flowed from surgery the men had performed to band some of the animals and insert radio tagging transmitters in the back or tail of others. The scientist insisted that this operation caused the heavily blubbered animals no pain. At first researchers had tried drugging the animals before tagging them but the drugs had caused fatalities. Now a bag is simply tied over their head and, though they resist at first, the beasts finally relax and the deed is done. I had been told that Weddells have no fear of man but the few females I came close to cried and their babies huddled up to them as close as they could. Perhaps they are fearless, but it did not seem to me that they relished being tagged, however painless it may be. As I tramped to the shack with my companions, I could feel the heart-breaking eyes of an 800-pound mother with a radio in her back reproach me as if I had done the deed myself. Of course, to be realistic, seals often look as if they were crying.

Why should scientists live far out here on the ice study- ing the Weddell seal? This temporary shack, designed to be rushed off the Sound like a piece of scenery when the ice begins to break up, has as its dominant feature a TV receiver. This is attached by cable to a camera that is five feet under the eight to ten feet of ice presently covering the water. A sound recorder is part of this equipment. Three men living in the hut split the day into eight-hour watches, monitoring the TV picture and the sound. The picture is fascinating. Beneath the ice the water is crowded with Weddell seals, all hovering around the sev- eral blow holes. The males waiting, the females teaching their babies, all of them alert for passing fish. Weddells emit four clearly different signals. These are all recorded, and all the TV pictures are taped. It is hoped that even- tually an insight will be gained by watching the behavior of the animals at the time one of these sounds is heard so that a partial understanding of seal language will be gained. The recordings, along with underwater observa- tion, may also show whether or not seals use sonar the way porpoises do, for navigation and hunting. The seals have large eyes, which to humans gives them a very sad and appealing look, but these eyes are excellent for hunt- ing. Seals also hear very well under water and in their sensitive ears there is a large bubble that may be the organ used in sonar response.

The basic purpose of the tagging by radio transmitting signals, providing a continuous record over a long period of time, is to understand seals' natural behavior patterns. How many hours a day do they spend on the ice, at what times of day, how do weather conditions affect them?

Census-taking of seals has been done from high-altitude aircraft, but at such distances the type of seal cannot be determined nor is it known if the photographs were made at the best time of day or under the best conditions. When the behavior of Weddells, for instance, is properly understood, it will be possible to take pictures at the times when there is the largest possible sample. A Weddell census is not entirely an academic matter. Weddells keep warm because of the insulating thickness of their blubber. Unlike fur seals, they did not evolve a thick luxurious coat of hair, perhaps because the wet fur would freeze instantly as they emerged dripping from the sea onto the freezing ice and into the cold air. Although Weddell fur is of no use, and thus they have been spared from extermination by hunters, they can provide oil and food, and some people consider their hearts and livers to be delicacies. Hunters from the U.S.S.R., Japan, and Norway, it is said, would like to take Weddells if treaty obligations would allow it. The scientists from Minnesota hope to show that killing Weddells legally would eliminate the species or, failing that, at least set a limit that could be taken. One may hope that the lovable-looking Weddells, unique in being the most southerly mammals in the world, may be saved from the extinction that could come about finally just from being hunted to provide a few barrels of animal oils easily available elsewhere.

Weddell seals interest scientists for several reasons. They are mammals dependent on air, yet they can stay under water for as long as sixty minutes and dive as deep as 2000 feet. How do they do this without getting nitrogen narcosis or "the bends" as a human would do? In addition, no mammal brain can survive without oxygen for more than a few minutes, oxygen supplied by the blood. How does Weddell blood retain enough oxygen for such long periods of time under water? Beyond this, Weddells always manage to find a blow hole before their usual immersion time of five or six minutes is up. How do they find the hole, particularly in the long winter when there is no light to guide them, and how do they understand that they have reached the point of no return and must go back to the hole they left in time to get a necessary breath of air? Furthermore, how do pregnant females make these deep dives? The embryo cannot be deprived of oxygen for any length of time or it will die, yet the female can stay down for lengths of time that, in human physiology, would certainly destroy it. There are some tentative answers to these questions. In deep dives, the seals' bodies do not fight the pressure from without but to a degree collapse under it. The blood circulation to most of the body is shut off at these times, leaving a sufficient amount of residual oxygen behind, and the circulation is entirely between the heart and the brain. In periods of light Weddell seals probably find the blow holes by eyesight, but in the dark use some kind of sonar mechanism, such as is well known in porpoises. As to the problem of the female diving deep while pregnant, there seems to be a mechanism which at such times provides a greatly increased supply of blood to the embryo, thus compensating for the otherwise fatal situation. Weddell seals are much too interesting to allow them to be wiped out to satisfy a few men's greed.

Because they are still hunted commercially and because they breed on islands in the Southern Ocean accessible to man, elephant seals have interested scientists for a number of years. These huge sea-going mammals are notable principally for their very frank social life. Adult males of many species fight to secure a mate, but usually these

fights are merely mock battles in which the winner suc-
ceeds by bluff. Elephant seals, however, really fight, and
the water is full of blood after one of their battles. All the
great bulls are covered with scars. The females form harems in September or October. There may be as many as
1000 cows or as few as fifty. The larger harems are divided
among several bulls. Only large mature bulls, usually fourteen years or older, are able to keep a harem to themselves
for a whole season. Younger bulls may attempt breeding
but do not remain around for long if a mature male observes them. Like Weddells, the female elephant seals
breed very soon after weaning but the egg remains dormant for several months. The pups grow very rapidly after
birth but there is a terrible mortality among the infants.
About one-quarter of the newborn are accidentally
crushed to death by adult males who lurch about clumsily
and heedlessly during the birthing season. Fighting among
males between their fourth and eighth years also causes
a high death rate, but those who survive the carnage of
adolescence may live to twenty years or more. The in-
stincts of male elephant seals make them difficult to keep
in captivity. Some years ago the Philadelphia zoo ordered
a couple for display. The male thrived and grew rapidly,
but the female did not last long. Another female was secured but succumbed, after eight months, due to exhaustion and the constant attentions of her mate. The zoo
officials decided that they would have to condemn the
naturally polygamous male to a solitary life.

Population estimates suggest that the Antarctic seas
have about two million Weddell seals but that there are
between six and eight million crabeater seals. Crabeaters
live mostly in and about pack ice and their floating home
is seldom studied by biologists, and so they are very little

known. It is realized, however, that their name is in error
and that their diet is almost entirely krill. They, in turn,
are a favorite prey of killer whales, and many older animals
bear long, parallel gashes inflicted by killer teeth. Although crabeaters usually live far out at sea, some of them
wander in a manner that scientists find extremely puz-
zling. Explorers have found the mummies of crabeaters
300 miles inland in mountain areas several thousand feet
above sea level. No one has been able to offer any completely satisfactory explanation as to why and how they
got there. (The mummified remains of penguins have
also been found in similar areas but this startling fact is
of no help in providing an answer.)

The leopard seals of the Antarctic are more easily found
than the crabeaters because they hover around penguin
rookeries. These predators take a toll of all penguin
breeds. After a capture, the leopard seal bites off the
penguin's feet, slaps its skin off on the water's surface and
swallows the remains whole. Around the Falkland Islands
they have the reputation of attacking small boats. They
have been seen upsetting an ice floe in order to knock
penguins resting on it off into the water. On snow leopard
seals can move more swiftly than a man. Unfortunately
(for sentimentalists) they are not hunted since their coat
has no commercial value.

The Antarctic has one other species of seal, the Ross
seal, but it usually lives in the pack ice, is seldom seen by
man, and is estimated to make up less than one percent of
the total seal population. It lives on a simple diet of krill.

The biology of the supposedly desolate Antarctic does
not end with these species. Of these the most conspicuous
are, naturally, the birds that fly. Among the islands there
are many breeds of albatross, fulmars, terns, skuas, and

petrel. Among the terns is the Arctic species, famous as the world's champion long-distance migrant. These amazing birds nest in places like Greenland, Labrador, and Siberia and then migrate 10,000 miles or so to winter on the edge of the Antarctic ice. The very abundant snowy petrel is one of the three birds that actually nest on the continent itself. The skuas also nest on land, usually right alongside penguin rookeries. Because of their penguin depradations, skuas are much disliked by scientists but are frequently studied because of their relation to that much more favored kind of bird.

On the land there is a very poor assembly of small plants such as lichens, algae, mosses, fungi, bacteria, and liverworts. Other than birds, the only indigenous land animals are invertebrates like protozoa, mites, nematodes, rotifers, and some primitive insects. A considerable number of scientists are concerned with describing the species and studying their environment.

Although considerable research activity goes on corcerning the fish that abound in the Southern Ocean, not very much is known about fish that inhabit those areas such as McMurdo Sound near the land. Certainly fish do live in these largely unexplored waters, since penguins and seals feed on them. It is known that some of them remain active all winter under many feet of ice. What do they eat? Plants are their natural diet, plants that can survive only by photosynthesis, a reaction to sunlight. How do the plants live through the long polar night? Two large species of McMurdo fish, members of the trout family, one named after Carsten Borchgrevink, leader of the first party to winter over on the Antarctic mainland, the other after Sir Douglas Mawson, a prominent Australian polar explorer, are actually bloodless. They have no hemoglobin, the red blood cells. They do, however, have a fluid that resembles blood in other respects. This fluid clots at zero degrees Centigrade but will not at 20 degrees Centigrade. The average temperature of the water in the Sound is 1.85 degrees Centigrade and they thrive on this. If it gets as hot as 6 degrees, they cannot live. No other animal's heart could beat at such low temperatures as these fish require. To understand such matters the biochemists are studying the proteins of the fish blood and muscle.

A problem arises here in that no one has ever been able to catch a Borchgrevink or a Dawson by ordinary fishing methods, even when the Sound is ice-free. So Dr. Robert Feeney of the University of California had a hole dug out on the Sound through twelve feet of ice, eight miles away from McMurdo, and put a little hut over it. Weddell seals spotted it as an airhole and come to it frequently to breathe. *They* are able to catch the exotic fish and often arrive with one, weighing between 50 and 150 pounds, in their mouths. Dr. Feeney or his assistants, waiting patiently in their hut, simply snatch the fish away from the Weddells. The poor seals can do nothing about this but simply go away and return with another catch. It seems that the Weddells are quite slow learners.

Rather than depend on Weddells, scientists have tried diving under the ice to see what lives there. One man had stayed down in the water for two hours, but forty-five minutes of diving was the average. Scientists want to cross this barrier in a submersible, a miniature submarine that could remain motionless for hours and use human observers, sound recording gear, and still and movie cameras. Nets could be used to catch Antarctic trout and the elusive squid. Some day there may be an article titled "My Day Beneath the Ross Ice Shelf."

CHAPTER IX

THE McMURDO CROSSROAD

At the beginning of each new scientific season McMurdo Station becomes a very busy crossroads. Scientists and military men flying in from the States and New Zealand, men who had wintered over at the remote stations and at McMurdo going home, other men going out to relieve them, scientific parties waiting for transportation to distant places, diplomatic guests from nations that had signed the treaty, newspaper guests asking questions, the men running the base and the fliers who piloted the planes, all these active people are there because the United States supports Antarctic research. And, the season when I saw the station, a small group of women were there as well. The introduction of ladies did not cause any turmoil then, though it might well have in the middle of a lonely dark winter. In any case, four of the women were married and all of them were disguised in costumes guaranteed to hide their charms.

The visiting press found themselves as occupied as anyone with more immediate business. No one found time to sit around a hot stove thinking about how cold it was outside. An absolute must was the visit to the nuclear power plant half-way up Observation Hill. To bring an atomic installation to the Antarctic was a daring political decision. It was also a feat of engineering. A mobile plant designed to be carried any place in the world, it arrived from the United States via U.S. Navy cargo ship and went into operation in 1964. It represents a tremendous saving in fuel, for power and heat, that need not be shipped in. Furthermore, it fuels a water distillation plant that gives McMurdo much of the fresh water it has. The plant can produce 28,000 gallons of water per day but at the height of the season, such as the time of our visit, the population is too great and water rationing has to be ordered. (We were told we could take one shower a week.) As we were shown through the installation, we noticed a great deal of steam escaping from the distiller. It was explained that there was a defective valve but the plant could not be shut down to repair it because the base only had about two days' water in reserve. The water is pumped up from the Sound, from underneath the ice, the salt removed from it by process of distillation, and then returned to the sea from which it came. The process is not very efficient. Only ten percent of the water removed can be made fresh and the remaining ninety percent is sent back down the hill at a temperature of eighty or ninety degrees. This is not hot enough to be used for heating the base.

The radioactive core is surrounded by all the customary safeguards. One core lasts for more than a year and there is always a spare on hand. When a core is removed, it takes a year before it has cooled off sufficiently to be returned to the United States. All radioactive wastes and cores are taken back for burial because, by international treaty, they cannot be disposed of in the Antarctic. Since nothing on the continent is classified, the nuclear plant is open to inspection by the Russians or representatives of any treaty nation. And, as the officer in charge told us, if the United States wanted to pull out in a hurry, it would be unable to do so. Someone would have to wait around until the core was ready to travel.

The top of Observation Hill, above the atomic plant, is another almost required tourist attraction. This 700-foot cone is composed of volcanic rock and ash. On its peak, men from Scott's base at Cape Evans erected a cross in honor of their lost leader just before they sailed on their melancholy journey home. Made of heavy ship's timber, a wood called jarrah, it took two days for the men to get it up the steep hill. On it they carved the names of the men who had died on the return from the Pole and then, at the suggestion of Cherry-Garrard, one of the scientists added a quote from Tennyson's *Ulysses:* "To strive, to seek, to find, and not to yield." The inscription is still legible today. So are the initials of various men who climbed to view it later. Such vandalism has upset Admiral Welch, among others. They cannot understand why people would dese- crate a memorial. The Admiral would like to post a guard over it, but of course he has no men for such a task. Hu- mans will be humans, even in the Antarctic.

To know how it felt to be a modern explorer, it was arranged that we would all get a chance to ride on a snow toboggan. Down the steep hill we went and out onto McMurdo Sound a short way. The motor toboggan was waiting for us. We stopped and a few of us got out to have the first part of the run. It was ten o'clock at night and cloudy. The light was rather strange, not quite bright enough to read by. Toward the shore there was a large flock of noisy birds. Skuas, we were told, the enemies of penguins, scavenging the McMurdo garbage dump. As we were about to take off a small vehicle came around a point of land, its lights on, and preceded by a man on foot. "I wouldn't go out there if I were you. It's just fogged in and you can't see your hand in front of your face." Jack Renirie, in whose charge we were, accepted this good council. He did not want to lose his eight guests, perhaps down some crevice, and perhaps he did not want to lose himself either. (Only two USARP people have lost their lives down there, one in an airplane accident, the other lost his way somewhere outside Byrd Station and was never seen again.)

Jack did not want to disappoint us completely so we all took brief turns on the motor toboggan, swinging in a wide circle out on the ice, but always within sight of land. It was fun but would have been more so if we could have really cut loose and go flying along at top speed. No one plays games, however, on McMurdo Sound when the weather turns tricky.

Even when nothing was officially scheduled, one could learn more about the science activities. One evening I was asked to visit the NSF offices. There the young ladies from Ohio State University, Dr. Lois Jones, Eileen McSaveney, Terry Lee Tickhill, and Kay Lindsay, were to be interviewed by the New Zealand broadcasting system over radio telephone. This was the first year that women scientists had ever worked in the Antarctic, and the press was being encouraged to make the most of it. Ever since their trip had been announced the girls had been photographed for television and newspapers, asked the same questions by reporters everywhere they visited until now, on the eve of actually getting out into the field, they were heartily sick of the publicity. The questions from New Zealand were banal and condescending, as if the women were some kind of freaks rather than qualified research workers. They answered, however, with forced good will, obviously hoping that this would be the last such ordeal before they went to work.

The research program proposed by Dr. Lois Jones was scientifically most respectable. It had been known for a number of years that within the Trans-Antarctic Range there existed two dry valleys, the Wright and the Taylor, that, although surrounded by glaciers, have no ice on the surface. The valleys do have lakes in them, Vanda and Bonney, and these naturally are covered with ice. The ice is about fourteen feet thick and the lakes more than 100 feet deep. The strange thing is that beneath the ice the water quickly becomes warmer. Lake Vanda's bottom water, at 200 feet, has been measured at nearly 80 degrees. The water at this level is quite fresh. Below this the water becomes saltier than the sea and also very much colder than the water above it. How can one account for these unusual lakes? Are they heated by volcanic activity from the earth itself or is their warmth due to some unusual kind of radiation for the sun? The answer seems to be that they are heated by both means.

Beyond this question, in the words of Dr. Jones, "four women scientists will investigate chemical weathering, salt content of snow and ice, the ancient geography and the limnology [nature] of frozen antarctic lakes, and the distribution and movement of glaciers in the area of the lakes." A general exploration, then, to learn how the valleys and glaciers relate to the lakes. Dr. Jones thinks they may be as much as a million years old, very ancient for a lake. The women will be taken out to the site by helicopter from McMurdo, live in tents there for twelve days (making their fresh water out of ice hauled from the lakes), returning to McMurdo at intervals to test their samples in a lab—and perhaps take a hot bath. During the radio interview one of the questions from New Zealand was whether the ladies planned to use lipstick while out on location. "Yes," was the answer. "It keeps your lips from getting chapped." Our press group wished the ladies well as they departed from their last interview looking very determined that they would ask no quarter from any male, no matter how rugged conditions might become.

Science did not even take time out for dinner. One evening, when I thought I was eating alone, I entered the cafeteria carrying a tray of food that looked impossibly good, as food always seemed to down there. The only place I could see to sit down was a table empty except for two young men talking busily away. Asking if I might join them, I was greeted with the cordiality that seems the absolute rule in the Antarctic. There is nothing too personal or familiar about it, just natural courtesy reinforced by the knowledge that everyone is in the same strange element and in a community too small to permit much friction. As seemed to be the universal custom, they asked what I was doing and then explained themselves. They were map-makers from the U.S. Geological Survey and had been at McMurdo about a week, waiting for a flight to their area of work, the Lassiter Coast, about 2000 miles away. This area, south and somewhat east of the Palmer Peninsula, is the least known, geographically and geologically, on the whole continent. I asked if there were no easier way to get there than flying 2000 miles from McMurdo but the answer was negative. No large airstrips

exist on the Palmer Peninsula and McMurdo is simply
the nearest base.

The first field party of six had gone to the Lassiter area
five days before, after a three-day delay when all flying
ceased due to the record solar flare and the resulting communications blackout. Finally the first six men to go to the
Lassiter Coast were deposited safely by two Hercules aircraft. These two planes, on their return, landed at Byrd
Station, nearly 800 miles away, for refueling. The Hercules
put down in near "zero zero" conditions, a whiteout,
caused by blowing snow and high winds, which leaves
absolutely no visibility. The crew of one plane was im-
prisoned within their cabin for ten hours because of the
conditions. The other crew was rescued after a siege of
only eight hours.

What with the solar flare and the whiteout, operations
had become quite a bit out of schedule, and McMurdo
was crowded with field parties waiting to be taken out
to their various destinations. At the same time 300,000
pounds of cargo, much of it necessary for field trips, was
waiting in New Zealand for aircraft to bring it down. A
side effect of the temporary overpopulation at McMurdo
was that water became very scarce. Showers were forbid-
den entirely and paper plates were used in the cafeteria
to save dishwashing. Conditions had improved, however,
two days before our arrival. The census for this day at
McMurdo was 994 people.

The map-makers I had dinner with were not particularly impatient about waiting for a lift out to the ice. Once
there they would be isolated for at least two months, living
in tents, climbing mountains, avoiding crevasses, well supplied with all the necessities of life but essentially on their
own. They would report in daily to McMurdo by radio,

if radio conditions permitted, but they would be at least as far away as Denver is from New York and, if they should need help, it would be some time before it could get there. Their work basically was to fix very accurately the longitude and latitude of various points in the Lassiter area that could be seen in photographs taken from the air. While they were doing this, aircraft would be taking more pictures and later the positions of mountains and other features would be matched with the photographs to create better maps.

The atmosphere resembled Christmas rush at an airport, homecoming week, an international convention, a resort in season, and the first day of school. The admiral gave small luncheons and dinners, the scientists had a cocktail party, an engineering firm gave a big, late affair, the Navy air squadron entertained, old buddies got together, and people who had just met talked as if they had known each other for years. For the news visitors all this socializing was ideal. With no trouble at all, in this little town bursting with 1000 people, they could meet just about everyone of note. If an encounter did not happen at one of the formal affairs, sooner or later most scientists and Navy men turned up at the bar of the officer's club. Members of the large group going out to the mountains of the central Trans-Antarctic Range, the prospective stars of the season, could be spoken to in an informal way. Their project was being billed at the "Highlight of the Antarctic Program." What they were about to do might become big news. They hoped to find the evidence that would nail down without question the proof of continental drift. In the past few years a great deal of evidence had been piling up in support of the theory (a heresy as recently as 1955 in U.S. colleges) that over many hundreds of millions of years the world's continents had been moving around. Now it seemed that a key question had narrowed down to the Antarctic and might lie in mountains just a few hundred miles from McMurdo Station.

CHAPTER X

A FIND OF THE CENTURY

THE Antarctic has posed problems for geologists ever since Scott's party found seams of coal there soon after the beginning of this century. It is stoutly believed that coal can form, after processes that take many ages, only in areas that were once semitropical and covered with dense vegetation. Clearly the frozen continent did not at present fit this description. Later expeditions found fossil evidence of plant and marine life that also clearly suggested a once warmer climate. To scientists who refused to accept the idea that continents had drifted around, the only remaining explanation for the coal and other fossils was that the axis of the earth had shifted in the past and that the North and South Poles were far distant from their present locations.

The idea of continental drift goes back at least as far as 1620, when Sir Francis Bacon suggested after looking at a map of the South Atlantic that South America and Africa fitted very neatly together. Late in the nineteenth century an Austrian geologist, Eduard Seuss, saw that there were many similarities in the geology of all the continents in the southern hemisphere and proposed that they had all once been joined together in a great continent he called Gondwanaland. A South African named du Toit found further geological evidence supporting the same idea. A German, Alfred Wegener, early in the twentieth century made an elaborate study based on geology and paleontology which he said demonstrated that the world had been one vast continent he named Pangaea. Those who scorned these hypotheses did so because they could not imagine any force on earth powerful enough to move masses as large as continents.

Then, in the middle of the 1950s, a geophysical revolution began. Scientists studying the dynamics of the earth started coming up with all sorts of suggestions unsettling to old ideas. This revolution of ideas may have had something to do with the IGY, at least it began in the same period, or perhaps it was simply a series of related ideas whose time had come.

A by no means inclusive list of the new concepts of geophysics includes: The discovery that the ocean floors are not much older than 180 million years. (Where were they during the past four billion years?) The finding that the Atlantic has a rift down its center and that it is spreading apart from this locus. (The other oceans seem to have similar rifts.) The finding that the world's magnetic poles have reversed themselves many times, that rocks of various ages point to magnetic poles that have moved radically in the past. (Analysis of sediments and rocks on the sea floor, in terms of changing magnetism, helps confirm the idea that the sea floors are spreading.) Evidence from many places all around the world that ancient lands had very different climates. Comparison of certain geological areas in South America and Africa that show them to be almost identical. Recent deep drilling on the ocean floor that even shows the rate at which the Atlantic has been spreading. Sir Edward Bullard's detailed fitting of the coasts of North America, Europe, and the two continents of the South Atlantic, done by computer, which show how they could have all been one. A similar fit between Australia and the Antarctic produced by Dr. Robert S. Dietz and Walter Sproll. New ideas on the forces that could have brought about such massive drifts.

Advocates of the drift theory wanted stronger evidence from the Antarctic than had been supplied by coal and fossil plants. Skeptics said that, if the Antarctic had once been joined to other lands, there must have been animals on the land, but their bones had never been found. For many years geological field parties sought such bones without any success at all. When the drift people finally did get their evidence, it was even more conclusive than they could have hoped.

The man who found this evidence was not just simply lucky. He was Peter J. Barrett, a tall, attractive twenty-seven-year-old New Zealander, at the time a graduate student in geology at the Institute of Polar Studies at Ohio State University. He was already an Antarctic veteran with four summer field trips in the mountains to his credit. Though not a paleontologist, a specialist in fossils, he had taken some courses in the subject and knew what finding vertebrate remains would mean scientifically. In the summer season of 1967–68, however, he was down on the ice, on a grant from the U.S. National Science Foundation, to look at the rocks in the Queen Maud Range and sort out their complicated history.

In his own words, "On December 26 our four-man party was landed with two motor toboggans, tents, food and fuel for six weeks by a C-130 Hercules of the U.S. Navy at the Otway Massif, an isolated group of peaks near the edge of the South Polar Plateau at the head of the Beardmore Glacier. Although the sun was out it was chilly—the temperature was below 0° F and there was a steady 10 knot breeze that we later found characterized the place. Next day Dave Elliot and Ralph Baillie [also from Ohio State] moved their camp eight miles up a glacier into the middle of the Massif, while Dave Johnston and I sledged north across the Mill Stream Glacier. The first five hours of the journey were cold, due to the Otway breeze, and without interest apart from the several patches of crevasses scattered across the glacier. It was with some relief that we crossed into the 'headwaters' of the Snakeskin Glacier, named presumably for its mottled appearance from the extensive areas of blue ice. About this time the wind died away and we began to warm up. Our goal for the day, the west ridge of Graphite Peak, was now in sight. By 11:30 P.M., four hours later, we were setting up the tent in a cosy sheltered trough of snow on the edge of the glacier within walking distance of the strata we were to measure in the next day or so.

"There were several places in the Snakeskin Glacier area that I wanted to look over. These were ridges or faces where the largest thicknesses of strata, providing the most complete record of the local geological history, were exposed. The localities were determined beforehand by air photo examination, though a geological report from the 1961–62 season played the largest part in the decision to visit Graphite Peak. It described a thick section, 2500 feet of strata, going from Permian [230 million years ago] coal measure to a . . . sequence that sounded identical to Triassic beds I saw in the Queen Alexandra Range, 100 miles north, the previous season.

"The following morning (December 28) was as warm and still as the previous evening, in spite of the thermometer which registered 0° F. By around 8 P.M. that evening we had measured, described and collected from about 1200 feet of strata and collected some very good plant leaves. Dave Johnston was picking away (this time unsuccessfully) at a green siltstone looking for plants, though with less enthusiasm than before; while I was crawling around on the top of a sandstone bluff about eighty feet higher up. [The altitude was about 9000 feet.]

"I was looking over some pebbles when an unusually dark pebble caught my eye. A second and more intensive look showed it to have a complex form and cell structure. A couple of excited shouts quickly brought Dave from his unrewarding task, and with much laughter and backslapping we agreed that there was little else it could be but a bone.

"Next day we returned and spent several hours crawling all over the bluff at the top of which the bone was embedded. Our only reward was a fossil gastropod mold, though it was interesting in its own right, being the first invertebrate to be found in this kind of strata. There was still an hour before we had to return for radio contact. We had photographed the bone so we decided we might as well try and chip it out. We hoped to get the whole block about a foot across out, so after a short argument in which each claimed that the other should start the work, thereby accepting responsibility for unfortunate slips of the hammer, one of us (I now forget who) began to chip out a channel around the bone. Three-quarters of an hour later, pieces of the bones were beginning to separate with the vibration of the hammering so we carefully picked them out and wrapped them in toilet paper. That evening we made radio contact with Dave Elliot and Ralph at the Otway Massif but contact was so poor that all we could get across were the letters, BONE.

"Ten days later, when we returned to the Otway Massif, the excitement was like finding it all over again as we unwrapped the pieces to show Dave and Ralph. Ralph who had had training and experience in vertebrate pale-ontology had no doubt about the bone's nature and thought it might be part of a vertebra or jaw. Later he spent a whole evening assembling the ten or so pieces and gluing them together with pancake mix."

When the summer season was over, the Ohio team of geologists flew back to the United States by way of New Zealand. There, at Christchurch, a customs agent, told that they had a bone, determined to quarantine it as bio-logical matter and sealed the box with a sticker marked "Meat Product." He relented a bit when he was assured that it had not been meat for many millions of years but still insisted on holding it in custody until the young men set off for the United States. Once there, Ralph Baillie immediately took the relic to the American Museum of Natural History in New York City to show it to Dr. Edwin Colbert, one of the country's foremost paleontologists.

Dr. Colbert did not hesitate at all in calling the two-and-one-half inch sample part of the jaw of a labyrintho-dont, a salamander-type amphibian that lived in the Tri-assic Age. Their fossils are common in South America and South Africa and varieties of the species have been found as fossils in Pennsylvania. Their characteristic teeth are very large and have an unusual folding of the dentine and enamel. The labyrinthodonts preceded the dinosaurs and there were many varieties of them. Some were as large as crocodiles and others small as newts. One thing they seemed to have in common, however, was their preference for fresh water. No labyrinthodonts would have been willing or able to swim across the thousands of miles of cold, salty water that separate the Antarctic from the other southern continents. If the animal did not migrate, then the continents must have. For caution's sake, Dr. Colbert showed the specimen to Dr. Donald Baird of Princeton University who absolutely agreed with the identification. Dr. Colbert then described the discovery as "one of the most important fossil finds of the century." Scientific journals naturally gave the event important space, and *The New York Times* thought this scientific story worth a position on Page One.

As has been mentioned, I went to Columbus to learn more of Peter Barrett's story and there, incidentally, met Dr. Dave Elliot who had been on the first expeditions. My first questions were about the mechanics of living far out in the field in the Antarctic. Dr. Barrett made it sound very simple. The altitude did not bother him. For a hobby, as a boy growing up in New Zealand, he had been a speleologist, a cave explorer, and he was used to living outdoors. The fact that night never came during the season was a help. If bad weather delayed work for a time, you could always catch up and work as many hours as you liked when the skies had cleared. Sometimes the Navy put up Jamesway huts (rather like the more familiar Nansen huts). More often field parties were given tents, but these were quite warm. The tents had to be pitched on ice so that the pins that hold them down could get a grip on something.

Barrett said that the Navy men believed it was impossible to survive on these expeditions, but he enjoyed them. Cooking was done on condensed-gas stoves. A man can eat very well. The basic ration is put up in boxes planned for a ten man-day period and these can be easily carried. Beyond this, a field party is let into the commissary at McMurdo and imaginations are permitted to fly. Out among the mountains at six or eight thousand feet, hundreds of miles from base, Barrett dined on foods such as frozen shrimp, French-fried onion rings, and frozen strawberries. While tramping up and down the mountains the men carry meat bars. When hungry or tired, meat bars can be eaten raw. In a written report, Barrett added, "They are pressed blocks of dehydrated beef, pork, salt, and suet, each weighing two ounces. They can be used to make soup or a dish like stewed ground beef. Opinions on their tastiness vary."

Dave Elliot gave me some background on why geologists study the Trans-Antarctic Mountains, the longest and most exposed range on the continent and explained some of the past history of the range as it is now known. Elliot would be a scientific leader of a field party going down there in a few months. Barrett planned to go back to the University of Wellington in New Zealand to teach. After showing me some photomicrographs, he told me a bit more about his Antarctic experiences.

He made light of the dangers there but admitted they did exist. On his second trip, sponsored by the University of Minnesota, he and a companion were out alone on a glacier. They were so used to the situation that they "cheapened the dangers." Barrett's friend suddenly fell sixty feet down a crevasse. The men had not been roped together so Barrett could have done nothing to halt the tumble. The man had a badly cut forehead and a sprained ankle. The weather was extremely cold. Safety doctrine in the Antarctic is that one man alone cannot pull another man out of a crevasse. This seemed particularly true if the man in trouble had a sprained ankle. Peter had to leave him for help and was gone for half an hour. With aid, he lowered a crevasse ladder and a lift line and got the man out before shock set in. On another occasion, the leader of the group slipped on glare ice, causing a very bad gash in his leg. The party was 7000 feet above their camp and already very tired before the accident happened. Barrett did not dramatize this at all. It was very tough, of course, but they made it.

Barrett's fossil discovery led to many things. The next year scientists looked more closely for specimens of the past and found, for the first time in the Antarctic, ancient fossils of insects. These were extinct dragonflies that closely resembled similar prehistoric insects discovered near Colorado Springs in the United States. Barrett's find also led to the formation of the large party now poised for flight into the mountains where absolutely conclusive relics might be found.

For the moment, however, the explorers' timetable had been set back by the delay in flights from New Zealand and by the numerous demands for helicopter time. The helicopters were certainly the busiest things around.

A schedule for a single day read as follows: "S-17 and S-13 to Beacon Valley. Three passengers and maximum cargo. Two hours at camp site for hut erection. S-12 to complete Skelton Glacier put-in. Two passengers and maximum cargo. S-43 and S-19 to Adélie Hut at Cape Crozier. Four passengers and maximum cargo. Two hours ground time. S-1 to Emperor Rookery at Cape Crozier. Five passengers and hundred pounds equipment. Close support for five to six hours. To Vanda Station pick-up and return four passengers and maximum cargo to Scott Base."

Such operations orders made it all sound very safe and simple. The trips we visitors took seemed delightfully easy. Yet there were hazards. On a routine flight not far from where we had traveled, a helicopter crashed and burned across McMurdo Sound, killing a New Zealander, down there to direct a documentary, and a scientist from the University of Wisconsin. Another scientist was badly burned and all the survivors were injured. The co-pilot and a crewman left the scene of the crash and walked five miles to a radio tent, but the set failed to work. Then they walked three more miles to another emergency radio station and succeeded in contacting the base at McMurdo. The survivors were quickly rescued and taken to the dispensary. This explained why everyone must carry survival gear, even on the most routine mission.

While the scientists waited to get to the mountains, they found time to talk to the press. Mrs. Pearson and I had a very lively talk with Dr. Paul Tasch, a paleobiologist from Wichita State University. He was a man with many scientific interests, but on this trip to the promising Trans-Antarctics he would be primarily concerned with fossils of fresh-water clams and shrimp from the Jurassic Age, about 160 million years ago. He would search for them in the exposed upper regions of the rock, one of the areas of the continent least buried beneath snow and ice. Having collected samples of various ancient species of these mollusks, he would then be going to Australia to look for similar fossil forms. If he could find forms in the two lands identical, or almost so, he would add another link to all the others in the growing chain of evidence supporting the idea of drift. Dr. Tasch was a late convert to the drift theory, having rejected it for years on the grounds that there was no force great enough to move such large masses of earth but, with the recent proof that the sea floor is spreading, in some places at a rate of two inches a year, he sees no argument against continental drift and much that is in favor of it.

I asked the doctor if shallow-water shells had never before been matched between Australia and the Antarctic, and he said, "Yes, of course." Then he went on with a phrase I am sure he often uses on his students in Kansas. "Science is like a Seurat." (Seurat was a nineteenth-century painter who developed a technique he called "pointilism," a method of applying paint dot by dot that seems to give a heightened impression of realism. Close up, a Seurat painting like the "Grande Jatte" at the Chicago Institute of Art seems like nothing but so many blobs of color. Only when you back away and see it as a whole can you appreciate the great design.)

What Dr. Tasch meant by this artistic comparison, obviously, is that science is just many, many little facts that are gradually, painfully collected until so many are assembled that no one can doubt the truth of the whole picture.

Another member of the party on their way to the mountains was a tall geologist, Dr. I. C. Rust, from the University of Stellen Bosch in South Africa. (As a comment on the difficulties of getting to the Antarctic, Dr. Rust had discovered that the easiest way for him to get to McMurdo from South Africa was by way of New York, across the United States, then on to Hawaii and New Zealand.) He had become interested in the Queen Alexandra Range of the Trans-Antarctics after he read a number of descriptions of these mountains and their rocks, the way they were stratified, the succession of various ages and types of rock, and suddenly realized that it was all very familiar.

The Queen Alexandra Range was extremely like certain ranges of the Devonian Age (about 300 million years ago) he knew very well in South Africa. No specialist outside South Africa had such a detailed knowledge of that country's geology and so he had been asked to come along and see the comparisons, and possible differences, at first hand. I asked whether, if the geology of the two places were actually so similar, he would expect to find either gold or diamonds, two things for which his own country was so famous. He replied that the object of his trip was, if possible, to add more evidence to all that was gathering so rapidly in so many ways in favor of the idea of continental drift. If he found either gold or diamonds in the Antarctic, which had known nothing but peace between nations, he would have a very serious dilemma. As a scientist, he would feel that he must report whatever he discovered, but that as a human being he would be much inclined to suppress the evidence and tell no one about it. The Antarctic has remained peaceful and a model of international cooperation because no one has seen any way to make money out of it. But if anything that men value as much as diamonds or gold should turn up, then the great dream of a whole continent dedicated to science alone would very likely be shattered.

It took several questions to find out why men from the Jet Propulsion Laboratory of the California Institute of Technology would be going along on this same expedition. They were biologists. What they would be looking for, in the mountains and also in the dry valleys, would be places where no man had ever stood before. Why would anyone be interested in finding such places? The biologists wanted to learn how to spot and detect microbes and primitive plant life. They were looking at the Antarctic so they could design equipment suitable for study of the land on Mars!

One evening the two men most prominent in the field trip to the Queen Alexandra Range of the Trans-Antarctic Mountains met informally with the news people in the living room of the senior science quarters, a room with a picture window and a view of some relatives of those mountains, a hundred miles or so across McMurdo Sound. The men were Dr. Dave Elliot, leader of the group from Ohio State, and Dr. Edwin Colbert, recently retired from the American Museum of Natural History, who had identified Dr. Barrett's labyrinthodont.

Dr. Colbert spoke of his specialty, paleontology, the study of ancient living things. Fossils from the past include actual remains, such as sharks' teeth and the earbones of whales, petrified matter in which minerals have replaced the original organic material, prints of leaves and carbonized traces of living material, the excrement of ancient creatures, and the tracks or trails of animals sometimes left in mud or sand. The fossil record is so complex and the fossil types so numerous that the study has had to be divided into specialties such as the study of microscopic organisms (such as the tiny shelled foraminifera), of plants, of invertebrates, and of vertebrates. Dr. Colbert was a vertebrate paleontologist. In spite of the fact that vertebrate paleontology usually only has mere fragments of material to study, it is saved from chaos by a very fortunate circumstance. It is unusual for any two species, even though closely related to each other, to have a *single* bone or tooth that is *exactly* alike in both of them. Thus it is usually enough to find one bone or one tooth to determine what species you are examining. Although Barrett's fossil was not much more than two inches long, Dr. Colbert found the identification quite simple. He looked at it, noted the rugose, or ridged, nature of the bone, observed various parts of the structure that even in this small sample are quite complex, and concluded that it must be part of the jawbone of this particular animal. It sounded quite as easy as many peoples' ability to recognize one breed of dog from another. Naturally it takes a lifetime of experience with fossils to be able to do this.

Although he was completely certain that Barrett's fossil was a labyrinthodont, he did not feel that it absolutely settled the continental drift question. "There is some niggling doubt. After all, it is an amphibian, and though amphibians today don't do well in sea water, who knows how salty the world was millions of years ago? And possibly the physiology of amphibians was different that long ago and they could tolerate salt water." What was necessary was the discovery of more fossils of land vertebrates in the Antarctic, and the key would be discovery of reptile fossils. (The reptiles were descended from the amphibians and took over world dominance from them.)

Dave Elliot seemed slightly burdened with the cares of being the scientific leader of a party that had started out as a group of nine but then somehow began to take on added dimensions. Although his personal interest was simply the rocks he wanted to study, he found himself concerned with logistics and with the problems created by an expedition that was receiving more attention than he was used to. He was a scientist unwittingly turned into a spokesman. He seemed happy to be able to say that he had just been able for the day to fly out to the Queen Alexandra Range by helicopter and choose the base where the Navy Seabees would soon put up, in a matter of hours, the huts where he and his group would live. Perfectly

aware of the interest created by the fossil hunt, he wanted
to make sure everyone understood that his own intentions
were serious and scholarly, and that he had not come all
the way from Ohio to hunt for scientific headlines.

To the press group he described his own area and gave
a background of the continent's geological past. In the
Pre-Cambrian era, a time that covers all the earth's history
prior to 500 million years ago and a time for which hardly
any fossil records exist, the Antarctic had many periods
of mountain building caused by folding and by volcanic
action and also much destruction of mountains caused by
water erosion. In the Cambrian Age, an era of about 100
million years, this crust was overlain by marine sediments.
After this, for an equal period of time, granite rocks, which
cooled slowly in large crystals, intruded into the crust.
These pink granites can be seen in the mountains bordering the western shore of McMurdo Sound. Then another
period of erosion began and the land was uplifted. Erosion
and deposition continued through the Devonian and Car-
boniferous Ages until about 300 million years ago, creating
the Beacon sandstone beds, the characteristic rocks of the
Trans-Antarctic Range. These beds contain many plant,
shell, and even fish fossils. Following this the Antarctic
experienced its first glaciation that can now be detected.
Fifty million years later the Antarctic was warm and full
of life. The common plant *Glossopteris,* also found in
quantity in South America and Africa, left its imprint of
a long and fine-veined leaf in the coal which began forming in this time. It was about this time also that the labyrinthodont, the fresh-water amphibian, lived. Then another period of deposition of silt began, adding another
layer to the Beacon sandstone. Between 200 and 150 million years ago there was a period of considerable volcanic

activity and many intrusions into the sandstone. After this came a long warm period when life flourished. Fifty million years ago the volcanoes of the Trans-Antarctic area began to emerge. Mount Erebus was born during this great period of convulsion, the Andes grew south under the sea into Antarctic, the crust cracked and folded, heaving up more mountains in the Trans-Antarctic Range. Ten million years ago the ice sheet began to grow.

The official description of Dave Elliot's project talks of measuring the various rock strata in the Beacon formation and collecting rock and fossil samples. (It does not mention vertebrates.) It speaks of mapping the geology of the area, determining its structure, and deciphering the history of the various rock units. To one who knows a little, but not a great deal, it would seem that all a scientist need do now to find out the age of a rock is to find it by measuring the radioactivity of various elements, but this cannot be done if the rock does not contain the proper radioactive elements. In such cases, dating must be done by the classic methods of comparing one strata of rock with another and finding fossils whose age is already known. In addition, Dr. Elliot planned a gravity survey, hoping to find a fault believed to lie at the foot of the Trans-Antarctic Mountains. He also wanted to find out the composition of the rocks that lie in the basement, below the Beacon formation, and make a comparison of Antarctic coal beds, usually from the Permian Age about 230 million years ago, with coal beds in Northern Europe and the United States from which they differ considerably.

Once all the hurdles were over, the two years of planning, the details involved with such a large party, the long trip half-way around the world, the delays at McMurdo, the greatest story of the Antarctic season worked itself out in practically no time whatsoever.

At Dr. Elliot's request, I quote the official release of the National Science Foundation as the most accurate account of what occurred.

"On November 23rd, 1969, *the first day of work in the field,* Dr. David H. Elliot of the Institute of Polar Studies and Department of Geology, Ohio State University, discovered fossil bones in a sandstone bed at Coalsack Bluff, Central Trans-Antarctic Mountains, about 400 miles from the South Pole.

"Since the initial discovery by Dr. Elliot, the exposure has been systematically explored by a group of vertebrate paleontologists, including Dr. Edwin H. Colbert ... [The release goes on to list several other eminent scientists.]

"As a result of this work, now in the initial stages of an intensive collecting program, various types of vertebrate fossils have been discovered. Included among them are the fossil bones of labyrinthodont amphibians, and various reptiles, among which the remains of thecodonts, characteristic of the Triassic period of earth history, would seem to be present.

"The current geological investigations in the Central Trans-Antarctic Mountains by the Institute of Polar Studies and the vertebrate paleontologists are an outgrowth of continuing geological study by the Institute of Polar Studies and, in particular, of the discovery of Dr. Peter J. Barrett in December, 1967 of the first fossil bone of a land-living vertebrate, which was subsequently identified by Dr. Colbert as a labyrinthodont amphibian.

"This discovery is of great significance to students of earth history. During recent years the so-called theory of continental drift has received increasingly favorable attention from geologists and other students of the history of the earth. This theory, developed in detail more than fifty years ago, supposes that the present continents are remnants of a once supercontinent, or perhaps two such continents, that fragmented, the separate pieces then slowly drifting across the face of the globe to their present position. If this theory is valid, Antarctica was once part of a great southern land mass known as Gondwanaland.

"The presence of fresh-water amphibians and land-living reptiles in Antarctica, some 200 million years ago, is very strong evidence of the probability of continental drift because these amphibians and reptiles, closely related to back-boned animals of the same age on other continents, could not have migrated between continental areas across oceanic barriers." *

A somewhat bolder statement came from Dr. Laurence Gould, scientific leader of Byrd's 1928 expedition, who happened to be in the Antarctic on a ceremonial mission and visited the find. He considered it "not only the most important fossils ever found in Antarctica but one of the truly great fossil finds of all time."

Perhaps the most significant fossil among all the bones found by the group was that of a lysostaurus, a not too distant relative of the labyrinthodont. The lysostaurus, according to Dr. Colbert, is a key index fossil of the lower Triassic and is found in all the southern continents. It is a *reptile*, a member of the thecodont family that is known to have flourished in Asia and South America particularly

---

* Scientific releases of this sort are always written modestly and with exquisite care so that each worker involved receives due credit. Quiet as the claims may read, to the world of scientists these authors are practically shouting from the housetops.

about 200 million years ago. Crocodiles and alligators are descended in evolution from this family.

The particular specimen found in the Queen Victoria Range was a fairly small, hippo-like creature, between two and four feet long. It had a peculiarly shaped skull, with nostrils high between its elevated eyes. This almost surely indicates aquatic habits. The scientists felt that the discovery established beyond further question the former existence of the great southern continent of Gondwana-land.

To those who had personally heard the scientists talk about their plans for this expedition, the news of their success had an extra dimension. When I reckoned that Dave Elliot had at last returned to Ohio, I phoned to congratulate him. He was modestly pleased with what had happened. Because of the various transport problems, the party had been more than two weeks late getting out into the field. The first station was beyond the Beardmore Glacier, over some of the Queen Alexandra Range. The Navy had built Jamesway huts for the group and they flew in aboard Hercs, landing on the ice November 22. The following morning, since the support helicopters had not yet arrived, Dave Elliot set off up a hill with geologists Jim Sharp and Leon Lambrecht towards a valley where Elliot thought he might find *Glossoptera* fossil impressions. With Peter Barrett, he had made a map from air photos of the area to be investigated and he wanted to see if, from a height, the map was correct. Coming on to Coalsack Bluff he saw bone-bearing beds. The bones occurred as small black fragments. It would be obvious to a paleontologist that they were not pebbles. They had a pitted appearance. Elliot only picked up two small fragments to show to Doctor Colbert. Back at the camp, the paleontologist immediately confirmed that they were bones. A great number of excited people went back to the location the same day and the following day excavation began. Before the scientists had to depart, they had made a large haul, though some specimens had to be left behind.

Dr. Elliot was naturally very pleased with the find. He did not speak about it on the phone, but it was he, of course, with Peter Barrett who chose the location where the fossils might be found, and it was he who strolled unerringly to the place where they lay exposed, who knows for how many thousands or millions of years. His word was for the poor men who were not involved with the fossils at all. They had a bad season. One of the helicopters was grounded with a broken roto tail blade, something that could not be repaired or checked out for safety with the facilities available at McMurdo. Thus, one of the three vehicles to be used for exploration was missing. In addition, their work was hampered by abominably bad weather. The second of the two planned sites was never investigated at all.

In the best tradition of science, Elliot was not inclined to linger long talking about yesterday's triumph. He was thinking about plans for next year's expedition to the Antarctic. It is a place that gets into some people's blood. I remembered a remark he had made at McMurdo concerning discoveries, an observation that seemed to me a very fine insight into the way scientists look at their life work. With each new finding, large or small, "One has moved the unknown one step farther back."

INDEX

Adélie Coast 112
Adélie penguins 15, 74, 112, 120, 129–135
airglow 62
Amundsen, Roald 4, 41, 73, 82, 88, 89
Amundsen Sea 111
Antarctic:
 Bottom Water 114
 Circle 21, 31
 Circumpolar Current 114
 Convergence 110, 114, 122, 123
 Peninsula 12, 111
 Treaty 1, 2, 17, 106
Arctic terns 146
Argentina 1, 12, 109, 111, 116
Amundsen-Scott Station 42
Atkinson, Dr. E. L. 90
Aurora 92, 96, 97
auroras 59, 62, 66
Australia 1, 9, 11, 15, 70, 77, 83, 112, 123
Automobile (first Antarctic) 76

Baird, Dr. Donald 163
Baillie, Ralph 160–162
Barrett, Dr. Peter 21, 40, 159–165, 173, 175, 176
Beacon formation 171
Beardmore Glacier 32, 39, 40, 46–49, 78, 95
Belgium 1, 12, 111
Bellingshausen, Baron von 4, 9
Bellingshausen Sea 14, 111

Borchgrevink, Carsten 146
buoys, instrument 116
Burton Island 12, 97
Byrd Land, Marie 14
Byrd, Admiral Richard E. 5, 6, 83, 105, 112, 174
Byrd Station 6, 13, 14, 29, 34, 38, 49–64, 154

Campbell, Lieut. Commander 39, 40, 46
Campbell Victoria Land expedition 85–88, 90, 91
Cape Adare 85, 89, 112
Cape Crozier 86, 134
Cape Evans 72–99
Cape Hallett 8, 106
Cape Royds 72–99, 129
Challenger 110
Cherry-Garrard, Apsley 85–87, 90, 150
Chile 1, 12, 109, 111, 113, 123, 127
Christchurch, N. Z. 7, 23, 25, 103, 161
Commonwealth Trans-Antarctic Expedition 13, 103
Communications blackouts 67, 105, 154, 165
Continental drift 126, 155, 157–176
Continental shelf 112
Cook, Captain 3
coal 79, 105, 157

(*Italicized words are names of ships*)

177

507.2   Briggs, Peter
BRI   Laboratory at the
          bottom of the world

© THE BAKER & TAYLOR CO.